McDougal Littell

Biology

Genetics
Unit 3
Resource Book

Evanston, Illinois • Boston • Dallas

ISBN-10 0-618-72524-5

ISBN 978-0-618-72524-3

1 2 3 4 5 6 7 8 9 - MDO - 10 09 08 07 06

Genetics
Unit 3 Resource Book

CHAPTER 6 MEIOSIS AND MENDEL

Section 6.1 Study Guide 1
Section 6.1 Power Notes 3
Section 6.1 Reinforcement 4
Section 6.2 Study Guide 5
Section 6.2 Power Notes 7
Section 6.2 Reinforcement 8
Section 6.3 Study Guide 9
Section 6.3 Power Notes 11
Section 6.3 Reinforcement 12
Section 6.4 Study Guide 13
Section 6.4 Power Notes 15
Section 6.4 Reinforcement 16
Section 6.5 Study Guide 17
Section 6.5 Power Notes 19
Section 6.5 Reinforcement 20
Section 6.6 Study Guide 21
Section 6.6 Power Notes 23
Section 6.6 Reinforcement 24
Chapter 6 Data Analysis Practice: Interpreting Bar Graphs 25
Chapter 6 Pre-AP Activity: Viewing Mendel Through a Modern Lens 27
Chapter 6 Pre-AP Activity: Chi Square Tests 29
Chapter 6 Vocabulary Practice 31

CHAPTER 7 EXTENDING MENDELIAN GENETICS

Section 7.1 Study Guide 35
Section 7.1 Power Notes 37
Section 7.1 Reinforcement 38
Section 7.2 Study Guide 39
Section 7.2 Power Notes 41
Section 7.2 Reinforcement 42
Section 7.3 Study Guide 43
Section 7.3 Power Notes 45
Section 7.3 Reinforcement 46

Section 7.4 Study Guide 47
Section 7.4 Power Notes 49
Section 7.4 Reinforcement 50
Chapter 7 Data Analysis Practice: Constructing Bar Graphs 51
Chapter 7 Pre-AP Activity: Incomplete Dominance in Four O'Clocks 53
Chapter 7 Pre-AP Activity: Royal Hemophilia 55
Chapter 7 Vocabulary Practice 57

CHAPTER 8 FROM DNA TO PROTEINS

Section 8.1 Study Guide 61
Section 8.1 Power Notes 63
Section 8.1 Reinforcement 64
Section 8.2 Study Guide 65
Section 8.2 Power Notes 67
Section 8.2 Reinforcement 68
Section 8.3 Study Guide 69
Section 8.3 Power Notes 71
Section 8.3 Reinforcement 72
Section 8.4 Study Guide 73
Section 8.4 Power Notes 75
Section 8.4 Reinforcement 76
Section 8.5 Study Guide 77
Section 8.5 Power Notes 79
Section 8.5 Reinforcement 80
Section 8.6 Study Guide 81
Section 8.6 Power Notes 83
Section 8.6 Reinforcement 84
Section 8.7 Study Guide 85
Section 8.7 Power Notes 87
Section 8.7 Reinforcement 88
Chapter 8 Data Analysis Practice: Interpreting Histograms 89
Chapter 8 Pre-AP Activity: Modeling DNA Structure 91
Chapter 8 Pre-AP Activity: Inborn Errors of Metabolism 93
Chapter 8 Vocabulary Practice 95

CHAPTER 9 FRONTIERS OF BIOTECHNOLOGY

Section 9.1 Study Guide 99
Section 9.1 Power Notes 101
Section 9.1 Reinforcement 102
Section 9.2 Study Guide 103
Section 9.2 Power Notes 105
Section 9.2 Reinforcement 106
Section 9.3 Study Guide 107
Section 9.3 Power Notes 109
Section 9.3 Reinforcement 110
Section 9.4 Study Guide 111
Section 9.4 Power Notes 113
Section 9.4 Reinforcement 114
Section 9.5 Study Guide 115
Section 9.5 Power Notes 117
Section 9.5 Reinforcement 118
Section 9.6 Study Guide 119
Section 9.6 Power Notes 121
Section 9.6 Reinforcement 122
Chapter 9 Data Analysis Practice: Constructing Histograms 123
Chapter 9 Pre-AP Activity: DNA Forensics: Solving a Royal Mystery 125
Chapter 9 Pre-AP Activity: Meet the Y Chromosome 127
Chapter 9 Vocabulary Practice 129

UNIT 3 GENETICS

Unit Project: Interpreting a Pedigree 133
Unit Project Teacher Notes 135

Answer Key 137

Name Period Date

SECTION 6.1 | CHROMOSOMES AND MEIOSIS

Study Guide

KEY CONCEPT
Gametes have half the number of chromosomes that body cells have.

VOCABULARY		
somatic cell	autosome	fertilization
gamete	sex chromosome	diploid
homologous chromosome	sexual reproduction	haploid
		meiosis

MAIN IDEA: You have body cells and gametes.

1. What are the two major groups of cell types in the human body?

____

2. Where are gametes located?

____

3. How many chromosomes are in a typical human body cell?

____

MAIN IDEA: Your cells have autosomes and sex chromosomes.
Fill in the concept map below to summarize what you know about chromosomes.

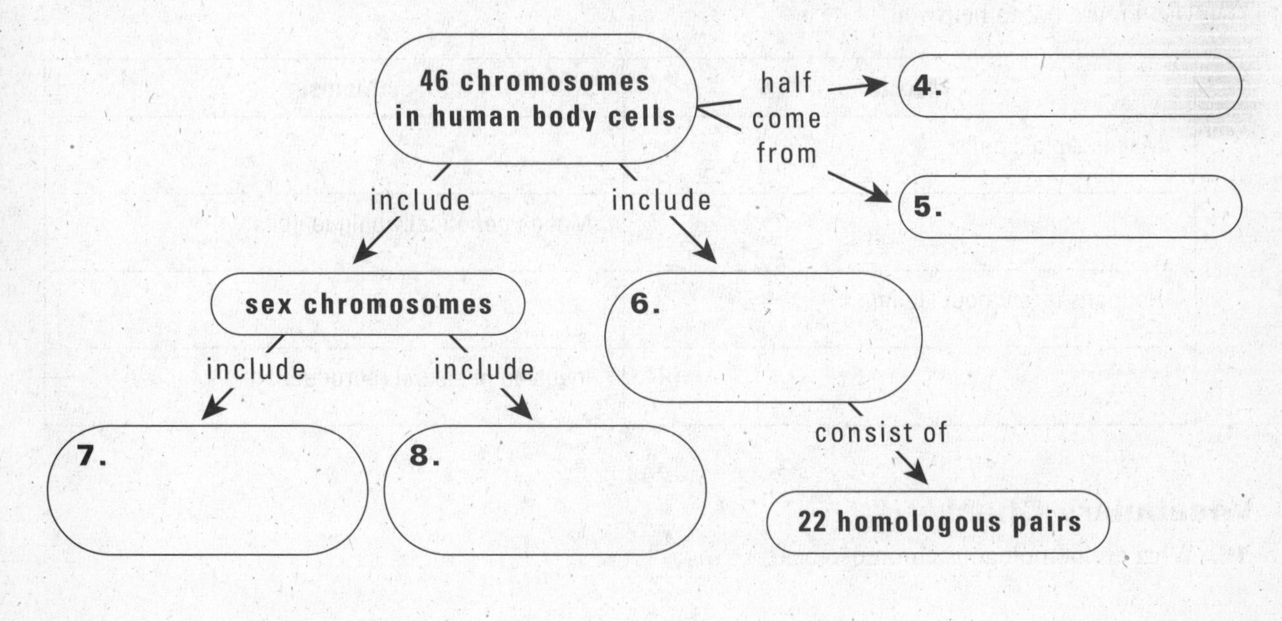

9. What is the sex of a person with two X chromosomes?

____

10. Which chromosome carries the fewest number of genes?

____

MAIN IDEA: Body cells are diploid; gametes are haploid.

11. What happens to the nuclei of the egg and sperm during fertilization?

____

12. What type of cells are haploid?

____

13. What is the haploid chromosome number in humans?

____

14. How many autosomes are present in each human gamete? How many sex chromosomes?

____

15. Complete the following table to summarize the differences between mitosis and meiosis. Use Figure 6.2 to help you.

Mitosis	Meiosis
Makes diploid cells	
	Makes genetically unique cells
Happens throughout lifetime	
	Involved in sexual reproduction

Vocabulary Check

16. What are homologous chromosomes?

____

17. The word *soma* means "body." How does this relate to the meanings of *autosome* and *somatic cell*?

____

Name Period Date

SECTION 6.1 | CHROMOSOMES AND MEIOSIS

Power Notes

Somatic cells:	Gametes:
• •	• •

Identify the items in the karyotype and explain their characteristics.

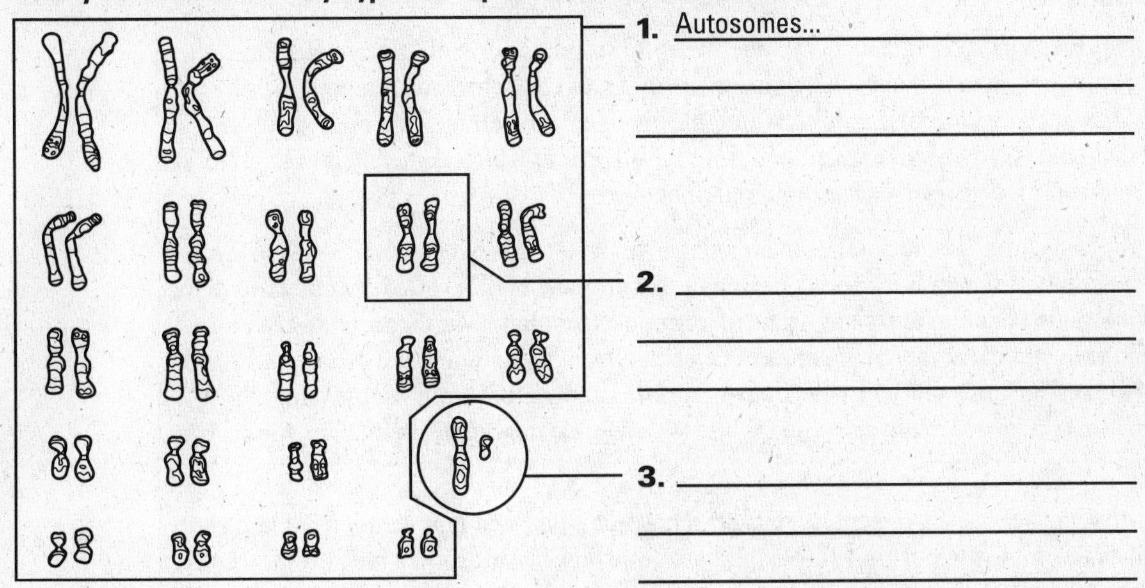

1. Autosomes...

2.

3.

Diploid cell:

Haploid cell:

Mitosis	Meiosis
• • • •	• • • •

Name Period Date

SECTION **6.1** | CHROMOSOMES AND MEIOSIS

Reinforcement

CHAPTER 6
Meiosis and Mendel

KEY CONCEPT Gametes have half the number of chromosomes that body cells have.

Your body is made of two basic cell types. One basic type are **somatic cells,** also called body cells, which make up almost all of your tissues and organs. The second basic type are germ cells, which are located in your reproductive organs. They are the cells that will undergo meiosis and form gametes. **Gametes** are sex cells. They include eggs and sperm cells.

Each species has a characteristic number of chromosomes per cell. Body cells are **diploid,** which means that each cell has two copies of each chromosome, one from each parent. Gametes are **haploid,** which means that each cell has one copy of each chromosome. Gametes join together during **fertilization,** which is the actual fusion of egg and sperm, and restores the diploid number.

The diploid chromosome number in humans is 46. Your cells needs both copies of each chromosome to function properly. Each pair of chromosomes is called homologous. **Homologous chromosomes** are a pair of chromosomes that have the same overall appearance and carry the same genes. One comes from the mother, and one comes from the father. Thus, one chromosome from a pair of homologous chromosomes might carry a gene that codes for green eye color, while the other carries a gene that codes for brown eye color.

For reference, each pair of homologous chromosomes has been numbered, from largest to smallest. Chromosome pairs 1 through 22 are autosomes. **Autosomes** are chromosomes that contain genes for characteristics not directly related to sex. The two other chromosomes are **sex chromosomes,** chromosomes that directly control the development of sexual characteristics. In humans, a woman has two X chromosomes, and a man has an X and a Y chromosome. The Y chromosome is very small and carries few genes.

Meiosis is a form of nuclear division that reduces chromosome number from diploid to haploid. Each haploid cell produced by meiosis has 22 autosomes and 1 sex chromosome.

1. How do gametes differ from somatic cells?

____

2. The prefix *homo-* means "the same." Explain how this meaning relates to the definition of homologous chromosomes.

____

3. How does meiosis relate to haploid cells? How does fertilization relate to diploid cells?

____

____

Name Period Date

SECTION 6.2 | PROCESS OF MEIOSIS

Study Guide

KEY CONCEPT

During meiosis, diploid cells undergo two cell divisions that result in haploid cells.

VOCABULARY	
gametogenesis	egg
sperm	polar body

MAIN IDEA: Cells go through two rounds of division in meiosis.

1. After a chromosome is replicated, each half is called a ______________________.

2. Two chromosomes that are very similar and carry the same genes are called ______________________.

In the space below, sketch the phases of meiosis I and II and write the name of each phase below it. Use Figure 6.5 to help you.

Meiosis I

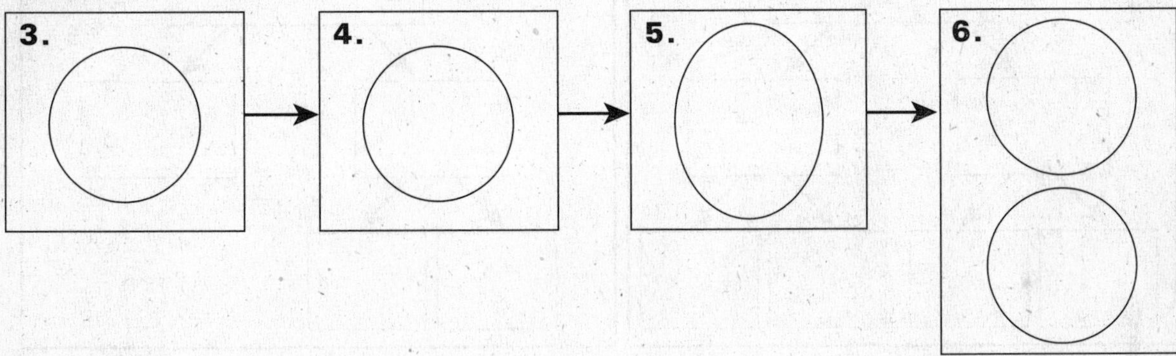

Meiosis II

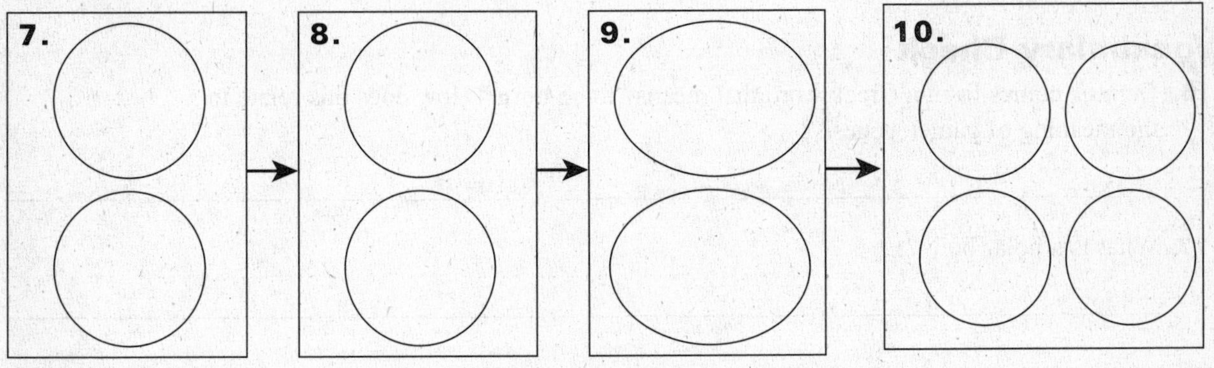

11. During which phase do homologous chromosomes separate?

____

12. During which phase do sister chromatids separate?

____

MAIN IDEA: Haploid cells develop into mature gametes.

13. What does a sperm cell contribute to an embryo?

14. What does an egg contribute to an embryo?

15. Where are polar bodies made, in the male or in the female?

Complete the diagram of gametogenesis in the boxes below. Use Figure 6.6 to help you.

Sperm Formation

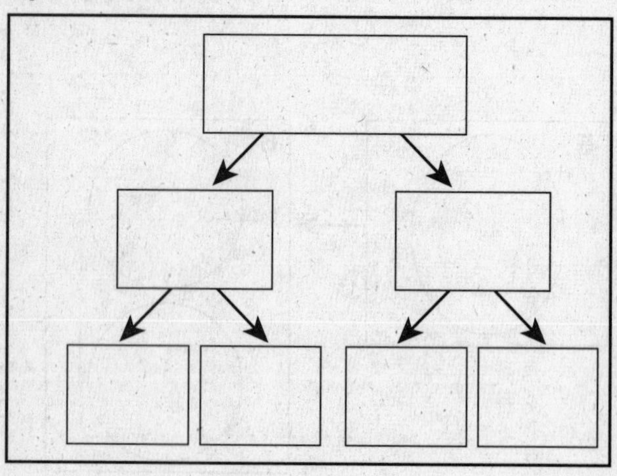

Egg Formation

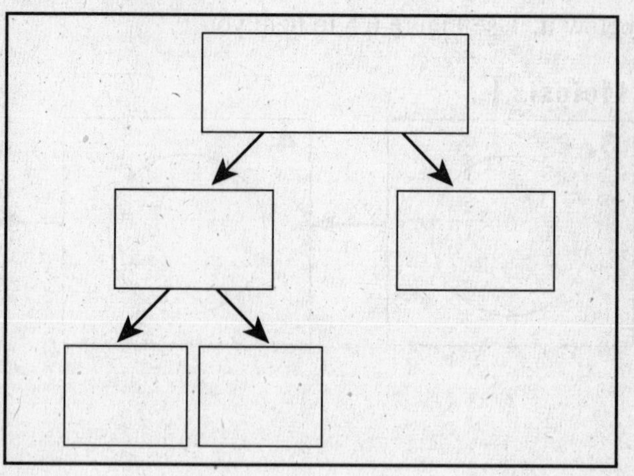

Vocabulary Check

16. *Genesis* comes from a Greek word that means "to be born." How does this relate to the meaning of gametogenesis?

17. What is a polar body?

Name Period Date

SECTION **6.2** | PROCESS OF MEIOSIS

Power Notes

Homologous chromosomes:	Sister chromatids:

Meiosis I

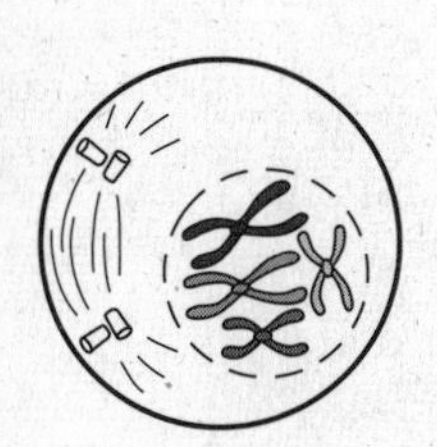
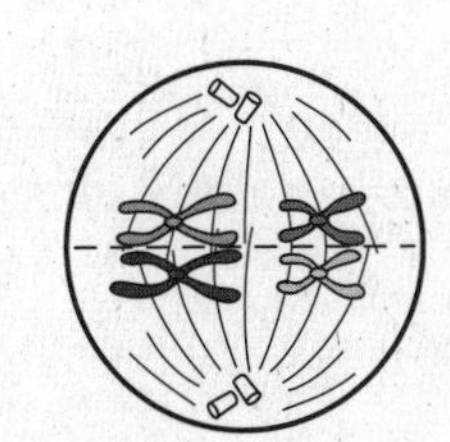
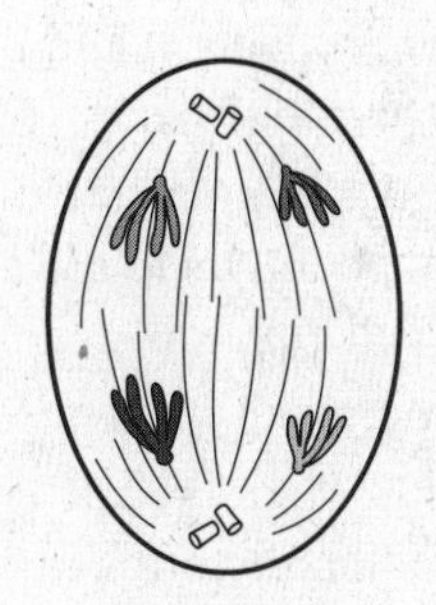

1.	2.	3.	4.

Meiosis II

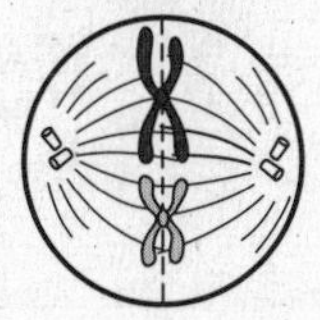
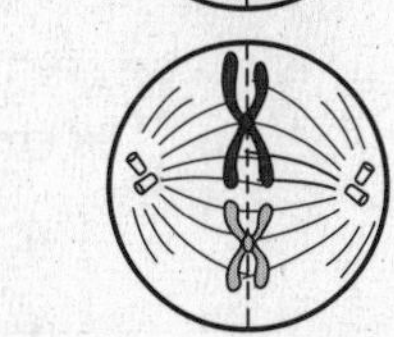
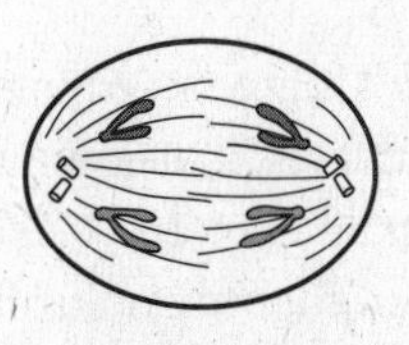
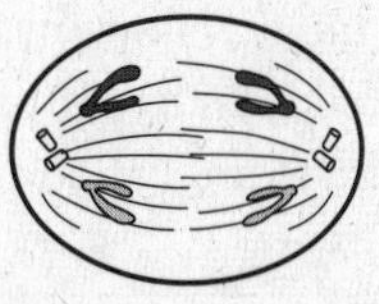

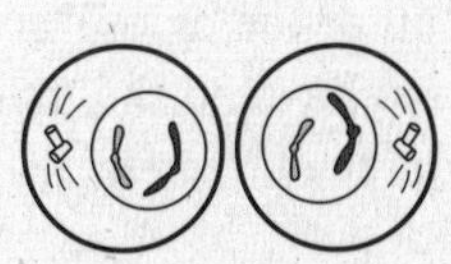

5.	6.	7.	8.

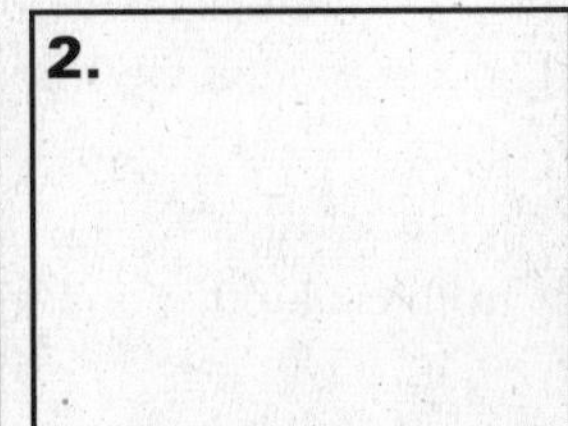
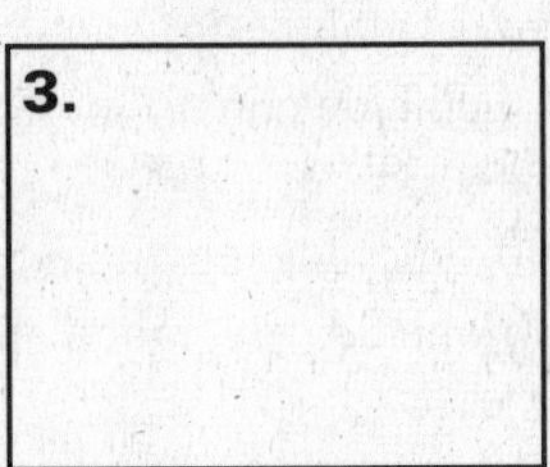
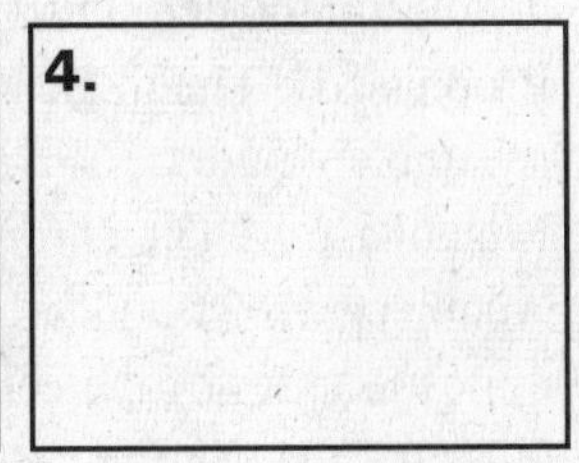
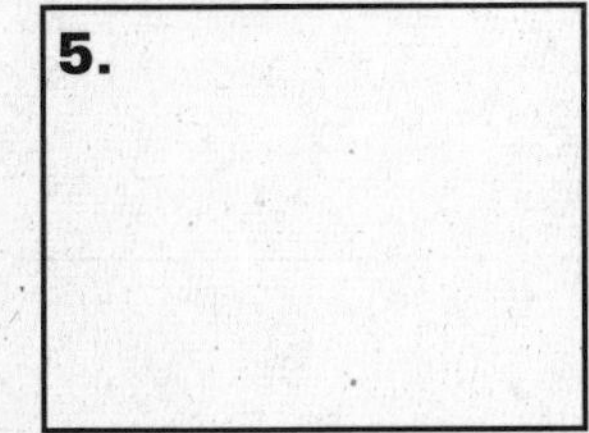

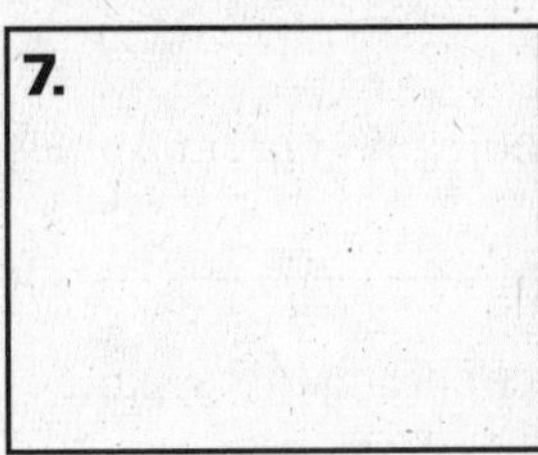

Name Period Date

SECTION 6.2 | PROCESS OF MEIOSIS

Reinforcement

KEY CONCEPT During meiosis, diploid cells undergo two cell divisions that result in haploid cells.

Meiosis occurs after a cell has already duplicated its DNA. Cells go through two rounds of cell division during meiosis. During the first round, meiosis I, homologous chromosomes separate from each other. During the second round, meiosis II, sister chromatids separate from each other. Meiosis produces genetically unique haploid cells that will go through more steps to form mature gametes.

Meiosis is a continuous process, but scientists have divided it into phases.

- Prophase I: The nuclear membrane breaks down, and the spindle fibers assemble. The duplicated chromosomes condense, and homologous chromosomes pair up. The sex chromosomes also pair together.
- Metaphase I: The homologous chromosome pairs randomly line up along the middle of the cell. Because this is random, there are a mixture of chromosomes from both parents on each side of the cell equator.
- Anaphase I: The paired homologous chromosomes separate from each other and move to opposite sides of the cell.
- Telophase I: The nuclear membrane forms in some species, the spindle fibers break apart, and the cell undergoes cytokinesis. Each cell has 23 duplicated chromosomes.
- Prophase II: The nuclear membrane breaks down if necessary and the spindle fibers assemble again.
- Metaphase II: The chromosomes line up along the middle of the cell.
- Anaphase II: The sister chromatids are pulled apart from each other and move to opposite sides of the cell.
- Telophase II: The nuclear membranes form again, the spindle fibers break apart, and the cell undergoes cytokinesis.

The haploid cells produced by meiosis are not capable of fertilization. They must undergo additional steps to form mature gametes.. During **gametogenesis, sperm** cells—the male gametes—and **eggs**—the female gametes—become specialized to carry out their functions. Sperm cells lose much of their cytoplasm and develop a tail. Eggs receive almost all of the cytoplasm during the divisions in meiosis. This is necessary for an embryo to have all the materials needed to begin life after fertilization. The smaller cells produced by meiosis in the female are called **polar bodies,** and they are eventually broken down.

1. During which phase do homologous chromosomes separate?

____

2. During which phase do sister chromatids separate?

____

Name Period Date

SECTION 6.3 | MENDEL AND HEREDITY

Study Guide

KEY CONCEPT

Mendel's research showed that traits are inherited as discrete units.

VOCABULARY		
trait	purebred	law of segregation
genetics	cross	

MAIN IDEA: Mendel laid the groundwork for genetics.

1. What is genetics?

____

2. Whose early work is the basis for much of our current understanding of genetics?

____

3. How did Mendel's views on inheritance differ from the views of many scientists of his time?

____

____

MAIN IDEA: Mendel's data revealed patterns of inheritance.

In designing his experiments, Mendel made three important choices that helped him see patterns of inheritance. In the table below, list Mendel's three choices and write an example of how he put each of these choices into action.

Mendel's Choices	Example
4.	
5.	
6.	

7. Why did Mendel use pea plants?

____

8. Fill in the sequence diagram below to summarize Mendel's experimental process.

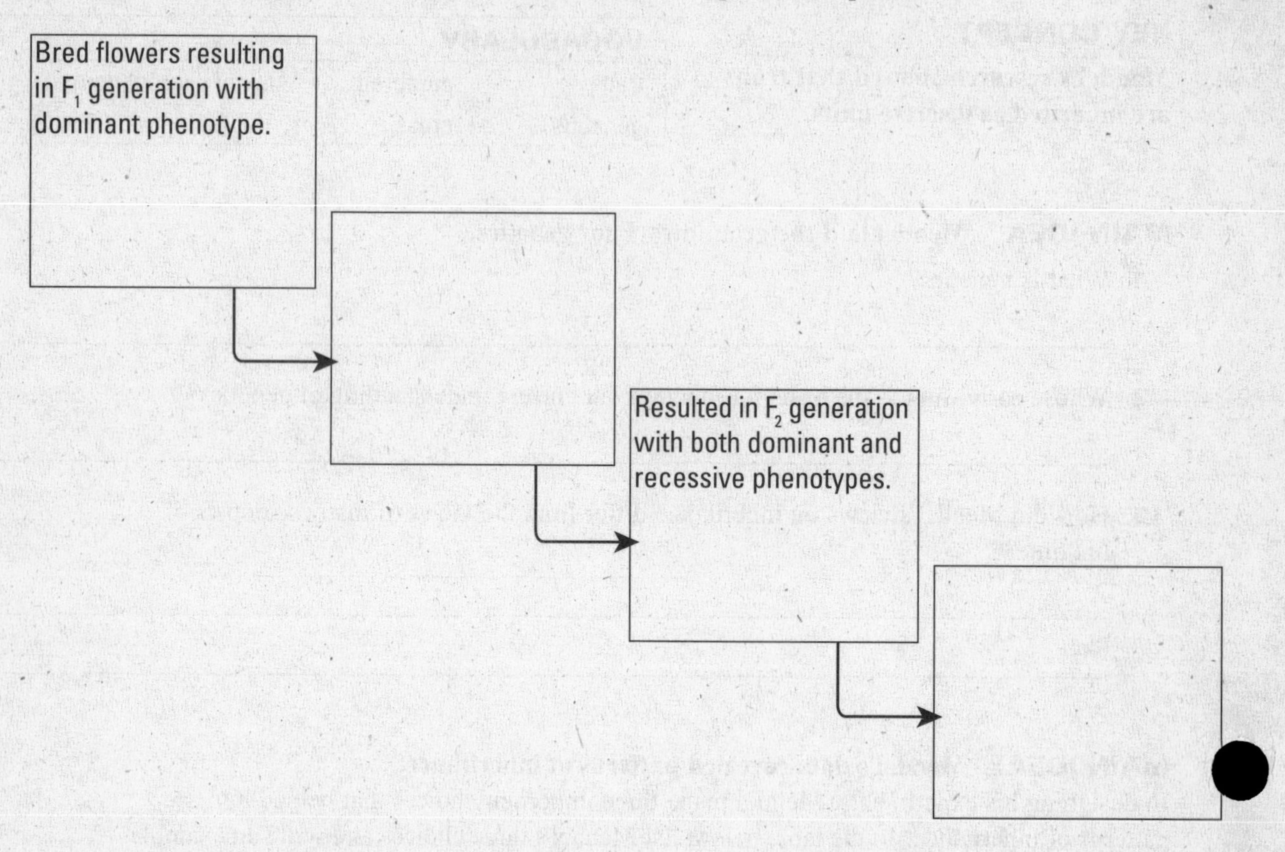

9. Mendel concluded that traits are inherited as "discrete units." What do we call these discrete units today?

____

10. What two conclusions make up Mendel's law of segregation?

____

____

Vocabulary Check

11. *Segregation* means "separation." What is "segregated" in Mendel's law of segregation?

____

12. What does "purebred" mean?

____

Name Period Date

SECTION 6.3 | MENDEL AND HEREDITY

Power Notes

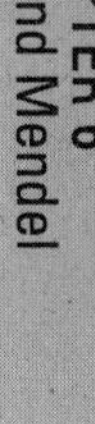

Mendel's Experiments

Three key choices:

-
-
-

Pea plant characteristics:

-
-
-
-
-
-
-

Cross:

- P
- F_1
- F_2

Results:

Conclusions:

-

Law of segregation:

-
-

SECTION **6.3** | MENDEL AND HEREDITY

Reinforcement

KEY CONCEPT Mendel's research showed that traits are inherited as discrete units.

Traits are inherited characteristics, and **genetics** is the study of the biological inheritance of traits and variation. Gregor Mendel, an Austrian monk, first recognized that traits are inherited as discrete units. We call these units genes. Mendel conducted his experiments with pea plants, which were an excellent choice because they are easily manipulated, produce large numbers of offspring, and have a short life cycle. Mendel made three important decisions that helped him to see patterns in the resulting offspring.

- Use of purebred plants: Mendel used pea plants that had self-pollinated for so long that they had become genetically uniform, or **purebred.** This meant that the offspring looked like the parent plant. Because of this characteristic, Mendel knew that any differences he observed in the offspring were the result of his experiments.
- Control over breeding: At the start of his experiments, Mendel removed the male flower parts from the pea plants. He then pollinated the female flower part with pollen from a plant of his choosing, which produced offspring referred to as the F_1 generation.
- Observation of "either-or" traits: Mendel studied seven traits that appeared in only two forms. For example, flowers were white or purple; peas were wrinkled or round.

Mendel observed that when he mated, or **crossed,** a purple-flowered plant with a white-flowered plant, for example, all of the F_1 offspring had purple flowers. Mendel next allowed the F_1 offspring to self-pollinate; that is, the plant mated with itself. In the resulting offspring, the F_2 generation, approximately three-fourths of the flowers were purple and one-fourth were white. Mendel continued to find this 3:1 ratio for each of his crosses, regardless of the specific trait he was examining.

Based on his results, Mendel concluded that traits are inherited as discrete units. He also developed what is known as Mendel's first law, or the **law of segregation.** This law states the following:

- Organisms inherit two copies of each unit (gene), one from each parent.
- The two copies separate, or segregate, during gamete formation. As a result, organisms donate only one copy of each unit (gene) in their gametes.

1. In which generation of offspring did Mendel observe a 3:1 ratio in the appearance of the offspring?

____

2. What is segregating in the law of segregation? When does this segregation occur?

____

____

Name Period Date

SECTION 6.4 | TRAITS, GENES, AND ALLELES

Study Guide

KEY CONCEPT
Genes encode proteins that produce a diverse range of traits.

VOCABULARY		
gene	heterozygous	phenotype
allele	genome	dominant
homozygous	genotype	recessive

MAIN IDEA: The same gene can have many versions.

1. What is the relationship between a gene and a protein?

2. What is an allele?

3. What term describes a pair of alleles that are the same? that are different?

4. Write a definition of homologous chromosomes using the terms "gene" and "allele."

In the space below, draw a pair of homologous chromosomes. Label the chromosomes with two sets of genes, one with homozygous alleles (Gene A, Gene A) and one with heterozygous alleles (Gene B, Gene b).

MAIN IDEA: Genes influence the development of traits.

5. Write an analogy to show the difference between genotype and phenotype.

____

____

6. How are alleles represented on paper?

____

7. Fill in the table below with the missing genotype, phenotype (dominant or recessive), or alleles (TT, Tt, tt).

Genotype	Phenotype	Alleles
homozygous dominant		
	recessive	
		Tt

8. If an organism has a recessive trait, can you determine its genotype for that trait?

____

9. What factors besides alleles affect phenotype?

____

Vocabulary Check

10. What type of alleles are present in an organism with a QQ genotype?

____

11. What is an alternative form of a gene?

____

12. What is the opposite of homozygous? of dominant?

____

Name Period Date

SECTION 6.4

TRAITS, GENES, AND ALLELES

Power Notes

Gene:

Allele:

Genome:

Genotype:

Symbols:

Homozygous:

Heterozygous:

Dominant:

Recessive:

Phenotype:

SECTION 6.4 | TRAITS, GENES, AND ALLELES

Reinforcement

KEY CONCEPT Genes encode proteins that produce a diverse range of traits.

A **gene** is a segment of DNA that tells the cell how to make a particular polypeptide. The location of a gene on a chromosome is called a locus. A gene has the same locus on both chromosomes in a pair of homologous chromosomes. In genetics, scientists often focus on a single gene or set of genes. **Genotype** typically refers to the genetic makeup of a particular set of genes. **Phenotype** refers to the physical characteristics resulting from those genes.

An alternative form of a gene is an **allele.** The pea plants that Mendel worked with had two alleles for each gene. For example, there was an allele for round peas and an allele for wrinkled peas. Genes are not limited to two alleles, however. Some genes are found in many different forms throughout a population.

Your cells have two alleles for each gene regardless of how many alleles are present in a population. Suppose there were 64 alleles of a hair color gene present in the human population. Your cells would only have two of those alleles, one from your mother and one from your father. If the two alleles are the same, they are **homozygous.** If the two alleles are different, they are **heterozygous.**

Some alleles are dominant over others.

- A **dominant** allele is expressed when two different alleles or two dominant alleles are present. Therefore, both homozygous dominant and heterozygous genotypes can produce the dominant phenotype.
- A **recessive** allele is expressed only when both alleles are recessive. Therefore, only the homozygous recessive genotype can produce the recessive phenotype.

Alleles may be represented using letters. Uppercase letters represent dominant alleles. Lowercase letters represent recessive alleles.

1. If you were to make an analogy and say that genotype is like blueprints, how would you complete the analogy to describe phenotype?

____

____

2. Use the letters B and b to represent the following genotypes: heterozygous, homozygous recessive, homozygous dominant.

____

SECTION **6.5** | TRAITS AND PROBABILITY

Study Guide

KEY CONCEPT

The inheritance of traits follows the rules of probability.

VOCABULARY		
Punnett square	testcross	law of independent assortment
monohybrid cross	dihybrid cross	probability

MAIN IDEA: Punnett squares illustrate genetic crosses.

Identify what each of the numbered parts represents in the Punnett square below. Then draw lines from each of the parents' alleles to the corresponding alleles in the offspring.

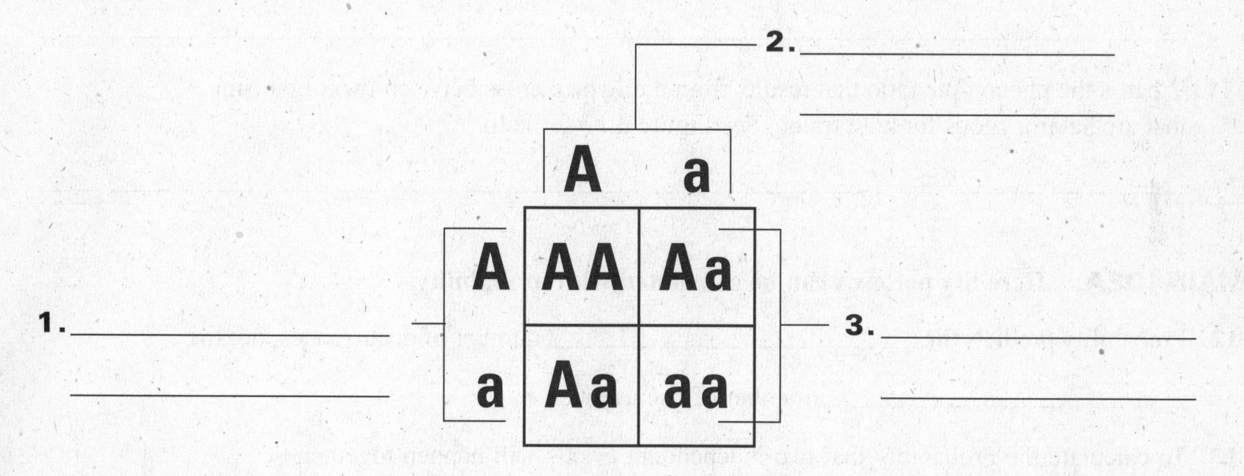

4. Why does each parent contribute only one allele to the offspring?

______

MAIN IDEA: A monohybrid cross involves one trait.

5. You know a ratio is a comparison that tells how two or more things relate. What is a genotypic ratio? a phenotypic ratio?

______

______

6. What is the genotypic ratio of the offspring in Figure 6.15?

______

7. What is the phenotypic ratio of the offspring in Figure 6.15?

______

MAIN IDEA: A dihybrid cross involves two traits.

8. What is a dihybrid cross?

____

9. Why does each parent organism in the F_1 generation have four alleles listed in Figure 6.17?

____

10. Suppose an organism had the genotype AABb. What two types of gametes could result from this allele combination?

____

11. What is the phenotypic ratio that results from a dihybrid cross between two organisms that are heterozygous for both traits? See Figure 6.17 for help.

____

MAIN IDEA: Heredity patterns can be calculated with probability.

12. Probability predicts the ______________ number of occurrences, not the ______________ number of occurrences.

13. To calculate the probability that two independent events will happen together, ______________ the probability of each individual event.

14. In Figure 6.18, the probability of getting one coin that is heads up and one coin that is tails up is ______________.

Vocabulary Check

15. What is a testcross?

____

16. What is independent in the law of independent assortment?

____

Name Period Date

SECTION 6.5 | TRAITS AND PROBABILITY

Power Notes

Punnett Square
- Axes:
- Grid boxes:

Monohybrid cross:

Ratios:
-
-

Testcross:

Dihybrid cross:

Ratios:
-
-

Law of independent assortment:

Probability:

Name Period Date

SECTION 6.5 | TRAITS AND PROBABILITY

Reinforcement

KEY CONCEPT The inheritance of traits follows the rules of probability.

The possible genotypes resulting from a cross can be predicted using a Punnett square. A **Punnett square** is a grid. The axes are labeled with the alleles of each parent organism. The grid boxes show all of the possible genotypes of the offspring resulting from those two parents.

A **monohybrid cross** is used when studying only one trait. A cross between a homozygous dominant organism and a homozygous recessive organism produces offspring that are all heterozygous and have the dominant phenotype. A cross between two heterozygous organisms results in a 3:1 phenotypic ratio in the offspring, where three-fourths have the dominant phenotype and one-fourth have the recessive phenotype. The genotypic ratio resulting from this cross is 1:2:1 of homozygous dominant:heterozygous:homozygous recessive.

A **testcross** is a cross between an organism with an unknown genotype (dominant phenotype) and an organism with the recessive phenotype. If the organism with the unknown genotype is homozygous dominant, the offspring will all have the dominant phenotype. If it is heterozygous, half the offspring will have the dominant phenotype, and half will have the recessive phenotype.

A **dihybrid cross** is used when studying the inheritance of two traits. Mendel's dihybrid crosses helped him develop the **law of independent assortment,** which basically states that different traits are inherited separately. When two organisms that are heterozygous for both traits are crossed, the resulting phenotypic ratio is 9:3:3:1.

Probability is the likelihood that a particular event, such as the inheritance of a particular allele, will happen. The events of meiosis and fertilization are random, so hereditary patterns can be calculated with probability.

On a separate sheet of paper, draw a Punnett square for a cross between organisms that have the genotypes Bb and bb. Use the Punnett square to answer the following questions.

1. Is this a monohybrid cross or a dihybrid cross?

____

2. What is the genotypic ratio of the offspring?

____

3. What is the phenotypic ratio of the offspring?

____

Name Period Date

SECTION **6.6** | MEIOSIS AND GENETIC VARIATION

Study Guide

KEY CONCEPT

Independent assortment and crossing over during meiosis result in genetic diversity.

VOCABULARY	
crossing over	genetic linkage

MAIN IDEA: Sexual reproduction creates unique gene combinations.

1. What are two ways that sexual reproduction helps create and maintain genetic diversity?

___

2. Which does sexual reproduction create, new alleles or new combinations of alleles?

___

3. How is the production of unique genetic combinations an advantage to organisms and species?

___

MAIN IDEA: Crossing over during meiosis increases genetic diversity.

4. Are chromosomes in a duplicated or an unduplicated state when crossing over occurs?

___

Use sketches to illustrate how crossing over contributes to genetic diversity. Use Figure 6.20 for reference. **1.** Draw a cell with four chromosomes in the first box. Make one pair of chromosomes large and the other pair small. Color in one large chromosome and one small chromosome. Leave the other two chromosomes white. **2.** In the next box, draw the cell in prophase I. Have each pair of homologous chromosomes line up together—large with large, small with small. **3.** In the third box, show crossing over between each pair of homologous chromosomes. **4.** In the last box, show what the chromosomes look like as a result of crossing over. You will use this sketch in the next exercise.

Refer to your cell sketch in the last box on the previous page. Also refer to Figure 6.5 if necessary. **1.** In the first box below, show what your cell would look like at the end of meiosis I. Remember, the result will be two cells that have one duplicated chromosome from each homologous pair. **2.** In the second box, show what your cell would look like at the end of meiosis II. Remember, the result will be four cells that have one (*un*duplicated) chromosome from each homologous pair.

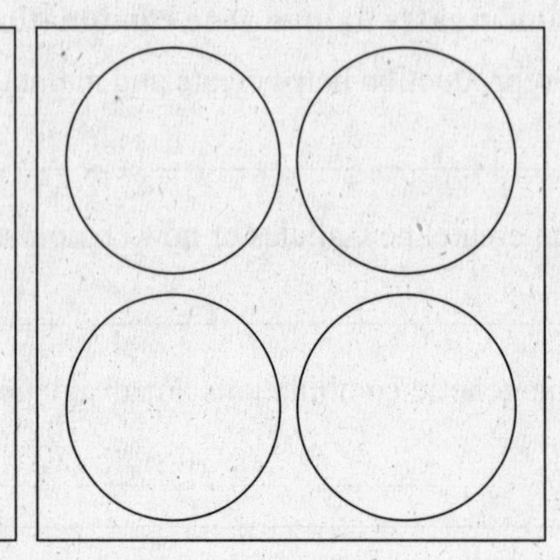

5. If genes A and B are located on separate, nonhomologous chromosomes, will they follow Mendel's law of independent assortment? Explain.

____

____

6. If genes A and B are located at opposite ends on the same chromosome, are they likely to follow Mendel's law of independent assortment? Explain.

____

____

7. If genes A and B are located very close together on the same chromosome, are they likely to follow Mendel's law of independent assortment? Explain.

____

____

Vocabulary Check

8. The exchange of chromosome segments between homologous chromosomes is called

______________________.

9. The tendency for two genes that are located close together on a chromosome to be inherited together is called ______________________.

Name Period Date

SECTION 6.6 | MEIOSIS AND GENETIC VARIATION

Power Notes

Genetic Diversity

- Fertilization:

- Meiosis:

- Crossing over:

Fill in the final box to illustrate crossing over.

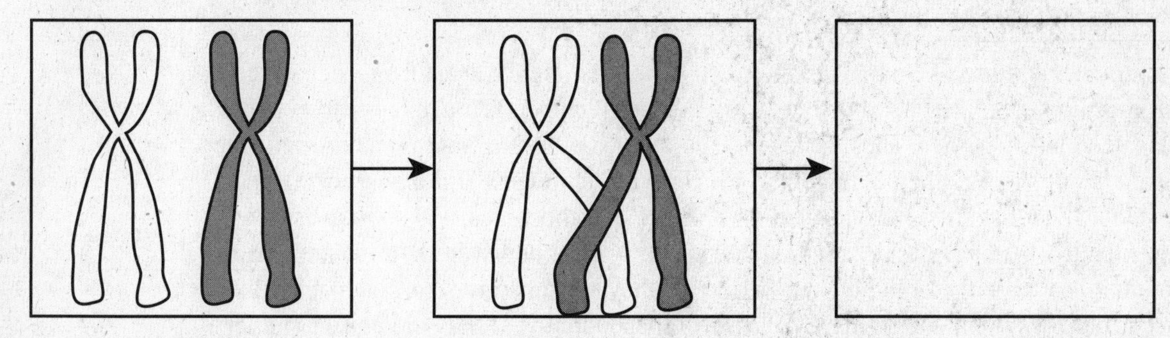

Genetic linkage:

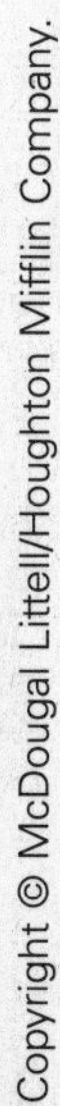

Name Period Date

SECTION 6.6 | MEIOSIS AND GENETIC VARIATION

Reinforcement

KEY CONCEPT Independent assortment and crossing over during meiosis result in genetic diversity.

In organisms that reproduce sexually, the independent assortment of chromosomes during meiosis and the random fertilization of gametes creates a lot of new genetic combinations. In humans, for example, there are over 64 trillion different possible combinations of chromosomes. Sexual reproduction creates genetically unique offspring that have a combination of both parents' traits. This uniqueness increases the likelihood that some organisms will survive or even flourish in changing conditions.

Genetic diversity is further increased through crossing over. **Crossing over** is the exchange of segments of chromosomes between homologous chromosomes. It happens during prophase I of meiosis I when homologous chromosomes pair up with each other and come into very close contact. At this stage, the chromosomes have already been duplicated. Part of a chromatid from each homologous chromosome may break off and reattach to the other chromosome.

Crossing over is more likely to occur between genes that are far apart from each other on a chromosome. The likelihood that crossing over will happen is much less if two genes are located close together. Thus, genes that are located close together on a chromosome have a tendency to be inherited together, which is called **genetic linkage.** Most of the traits that Mendel studied were located on separate chromosomes, and so they assorted independently. When genes are on the same chromosome, however, their distance from each other is a large factor in how they assort. If they are far apart, crossing over is likely to occur between them and so they will assort independently. If they are close together, they are unlikely to be separated by crossing over and so they will not assort independently.

1. What factors contribute to genetic diversity?

___

2. What is crossing over?

___

___

3. If two genes are located close together on the same chromosome, are they likely to follow Mendel's law of independent assortment? Explain.

___

___

Name Period Date

CHAPTER 6

INTERPRETING BAR GRAPHS

Data Analysis Practice

Bar graphs represent data using bars to show data points.

In the example below, students collected data about the natural hair color of 200 students, faculty, and staff at their school. The bar graph shows the results of their survey.

GRAPH 1. HAIR COLOR SURVEY

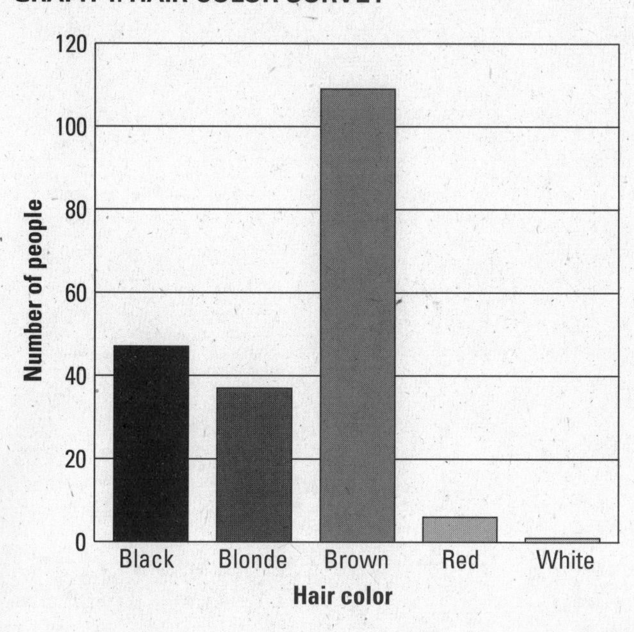

1. Analyze Which hair color was the most common? Which was the least common?

____

2. Hypothesize Based on the observations made by the students, form a testable hypothesis about how hair color is inherited.

____

____

____

CHAPTER 6 | VIEWING MENDEL THROUGH A MODERN LENS

Pre-AP* Activity

In Chapter 6, you have learned about Gregor Mendel and his research with garden peas. Mendel published his paper, "Versuche über Pflanzen Hybriden" (Experiments in Plant Hybridization), in 1865. Remember that he made his conclusions at a time when DNA, genes, and chromosomes were unknown. How can Mendel's conclusions be interpreted today?

The following excerpts taken from Mendel's paper deal with his observations of different generations of pea plants. Read each excerpt, then write an interpretation of each using the modern principles and terms you have learned. (Note: Mendel used italics for emphasis.) Here is an example:

> In this [F_2] generation there reappear, together with the dominant characters, the recessive ones with their peculiarities fully developed, and this occurs in the definitely expressed average proportion of three to one, so that among each four plants of this generation three display the dominant character and one the recessive . . . *Transitional forms were not observed in any experiment.*

Interpretation: When you cross two plants that are heterozygous for dominant-recessive traits, the ratio of phenotypes among the offspring is 3 dominant to 1 recessive. Simple dominant-recessive traits are inherited as discrete units and do not blend together.

As you work on your interpretations of the following excerpts, you might want to make a note of the meanings of specific terms Mendel uses, such as *forms, character, hybrid, egg cell, pollen cell, classes,* and *conjoined.*

1. "Those forms which in the first generation exhibit the recessive character do not further vary in the second generation as regards this character; they remain constant in their offspring."

___

___

___

2. "Experimentally, therefore, the theory is confirmed that *the pea hybrids form egg and pollen cells which, in their constitution, represent in equal numbers all constant forms which result from the combination of the characters united in fertilization.*"

___

___

___

___

___

3. When referring to the cross between two hybrid plants, Mendel wrote "The simplest case is afforded by the developmental series of each pair of differentiating characters. This series is represented by the expression A + 2A*a* + *a*, in which A and *a* signify the forms with constant differentiating characters, and A*a* the hybrid form of both. It includes in three different classes four individuals. In the formation of these, pollen and egg cells of the form A and *a* take part on the average equally in the fertilization; hence each form [occurs] twice, since four individuals are formed. They participate consequently in the fertilization:
pollen cells A + A + *a* + *a* + egg cells A + A + *a* + *a*
It remains, therefore, purely a matter of chance which of the two sorts of pollen will become united with each separate egg cell."

4. "The result of the fertilization may be made clear by putting the signs of the conjoined egg and pollen cells in the form of fractions, those for the pollen cells above and those for the egg cells below the line. We then have *A/A* + *A/a* + *a/A* + *a/a*."

5. When summarizing the results of crosses between plants that differed in two or three characters, Mendel wrote "It is demonstrated at the same time that *the relation of each pair of different characters in hybrid union is independent of the other differences in the two original parental stocks.*"

CHAPTER 6 | CHI SQUARE TESTS

Pre-AP Activity

In Chapter 6 you have learned about the probabilities expected in the offspring of genetic crosses. Here you will use a chi square test to see how much Mendel's results agreed with his expected results and hypothesis.

PROBABILITY

You can use Punnett squares to determine the possible outcomes of a genetic cross and to find the probabilities of each outcome. For example, in a monohybrid cross between two heterozygous round-seeded plants, two phenotypes—round seeds and wrinkled-seeds—have probabilities 3 out of 4 (3/4) and 1 out of 4 (1/4), respectively. Mendel observed the seed shapes of 7324 plants. If his observed results agreed exactly with his hypothesis, 75%, or 5493, of the offspring plants would have had round seeds. But in fact, Mendel saw 5474 plants with round seeds. Probabilities predict but do not guarantee the outcomes of experiments. If chance plays a role, how can we know that Mendel's actual results were not achieved by blind luck?

THE CHI SQUARE TEST

The chi square test offers a way to determine if differences between the expected and actual results of an experiment are due to chance. The chi square test is basically an equation whose outcome shows if an experiment's results are within 5% of the expected results. The variables that are plugged into this equation are as follows:

K = The number of possible outcomes that can be observed in an experiment. In flipping a coin, K is 2 (heads and tails). K is 2 for the possible phenotypes resulting from a monohybrid cross (dominant and recessive). In Mendel's dihybrid cross, K is 4 (wrinkled-yellow, wrinkled-green, round-green, round-yellow).

N = The number of observations or results. For example, Mendel's monohybrid pea plant cross yielded 7324 plants, so $N = 7324$.

E = The number of times you expect a specific outcome. This is determined by multiplying the probability of an outcome by N

In Mendel's cross, the dominant phenotype is assigned outcome 1 or $K(1)$. The recessive phenotype = outcome 2 or $K(2)$. Therefore, each N is labeled $N(1)$, $N(2)$, and so on, all the way up through $N(K)$. In Mendel's cross, $N(1) = 5474$ and $N(2) = 1850$.

Each outcome, or K, has an expected probability: $P(1)$, $P(2)$, and so on, up through $P(K)$. For a monohybrid cross, $P(1)$ is 3/4, and $P(2)$ is 1/4. From P we get E by multiplying it by N. So, $E(1) = N \times P(1)$, $E(2) = N \times P(2)$, and so on. In general, $E(K) = N \times P(K)$.

The chi square equation is as follows:

$$\chi^2 = \frac{[N(1) - E(1)]^2}{E(1)} + \frac{[N(2) - E(2)]^2}{E(2)} + \ldots \frac{[N(K) - E(K)]^2}{E(K)}$$

You square the difference between the expected result and observed result for a specific outcome, and divide that by the expected result. This yields a ratio. Do this for all of the possible outcomes, and then add up all of the ratios. (The more possible outcomes (K), the more ratios you have to add up.) The resulting sum, or χ^2, has a known probability distribution, called the chi squared distribution. There is a different chi squared distribution for each value of K, or number of possible outcomes. Scientists say that data are significantly different from the hypothesis if the chance of seeing a value of χ^2 larger than the one that you calculated is 5% or less. To apply this rule, scientists check whether χ^2 exceeds a constant called the critical value. Below is a table of critical values.

K	2	3	4	5	6	7	8	9	10
Critical Value	3.84	5.99	7.81	9.49	11.07	12.59	14.07	15.51	16.92

Applying the expected and actual results from Mendel's monohybrid cross to the chi square formula gives us

$$\chi^2 = \frac{[5474 - 5493]^2}{5493} + \frac{[1850 - 1831]^2}{1831} = \frac{361}{5493} + \frac{361}{1831} = 0.066 + 0.197 = 0.263$$

Since the calculated value of 0.263 is less than the critical value of 3.84, you can conclude that the data and the hypothesis do not contradict one another, and the similarity between Mendel's expected and actual results is not a coincidence or stroke of luck.

Answer the following questions on a separate sheet of paper.

1. Mendel hypothesized that the four phenotypes of a dihybrid cross should appear in the ratio of 9:3:3:1. The table below gives the number of times each phenotype appeared out of 556 plants. Convert Mendel's expected ratio of the four phenotypes into probabilities of each. Calculate the expected number—$E(1)$, $E(2)$, $E(3)$, $E(4)$—of each outcome (remember: $N = 556$). Record your answers in the table. Round N values to the nearest whole number.

Phenotype (*K*)	**round & yellow (1)**	**wrinkled & yellow (2)**	**round & green (3)**	**wrinkled & green (4)**
N(*K*)	315	101	108	32
P(*K*)				
E(*K*)				

2. Calculate the χ^2 from the data. Round decimals to the nearest thousandth throughout your calculation. Show your complete calculation with variables in place. Are Mendel's results significant? Explain.

Name Period Date

CHAPTER 6

MEIOSIS AND MENDEL

Vocabulary Practice

somatic cell
gamete
homologous chromosome
autosome
sex chromosome
sexual reproduction
fertilization
diploid
haploid
meiosis
gametogenesis
sperm

egg
polar body
trait
genetics
purebred
cross
law of segregation
gene
allele
homozygous
heterozygous
genome

genotype
phenotype
dominant
recessive
Punnett square
monohybrid cross
testcross
dihybrid cross
law of independent assortment
probability
crossing over
genetic linkage

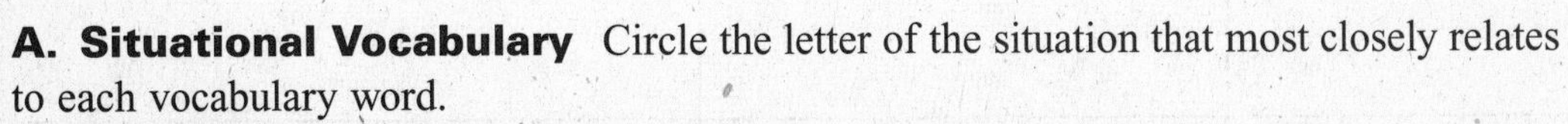

A. Situational Vocabulary Circle the letter of the situation that most closely relates to each vocabulary word.

1. **fertilization:** a) union of gametes; b) division of chromosomes
2. **purebred:** a) a scruffy mutt; b) a sleek Labrador retriever
3. **diploid:** a) a dollar; b) fifty cents
4. **sexual reproduction:** a) produces genetically identical offspring; b) produces genetically unique offspring
5. **trait:** a) inheriting your father's laugh; b) inheriting your father's watch
6. **homologous chromosomes:** a) carry the same genes; b) carry identical alleles
7. **Punnett square:** a) like playing tic-tac-toe; b) like playing rock-paper-scissors
8. **genome:** a) like a computer hard drive; b) like a computer screen
9. **polar body:** a) becomes a baby; b) becomes broken down by the body
10. **meiosis:** a) preserves chromosome number; b) reduces chromosome number
11. **testcross:** a) reveals phenotype; b) reveals genotype
12. **probability:** a) the likelihood a given event will occur; b) the number of times a given event has occurred

Name Period Date

B. The Same But Different For each pair of words listed in the table below, list one way that they are similar and one way that they are different.

SIMILARITY	WORD PAIRS	DIFFERENCE
laws of genetics developed by Mendel	law of segregation	organisms have two copies of every gene but donate only one
	law of independent assortment	characteristics are inherited independently of each other
1.	autosome	
	sex chromosome	
2.	somatic cell	
	gamete	
3.	sperm	
	egg	
4.	homozygous	
	heterozygous	
5.	dominant	
	recessive	
6.	diploid	
	haploid	
7.	monohybrid cross	
	dihybrid cross	

Name Period Date

C. Complete the Story Below is a story about Mendel's experiments. Fill in the blanks with words from the word bank to complete the story. Each word is used only once.

crossed	gene	law of independent assortment	traits
crossing over	genetic	law of segregation	
gametogenesis	genetic linkage	purebred	

Gregor Mendel wanted to understand how ____________________ were inherited, so he performed ____________________ experiments using pea plants. Mendel used plants that were ____________________, which means that the plants had self-pollinated for so long that the offspring always looked like the parent plant. He examined seven "either-or" characteristics. First, Mendel ____________________ a plant displaying the dominant phenotype with a plant displaying the recessive phenotype. Next, he allowed the offspring of this cross, the F_1 generation, to self-pollinate, and then calculated the phenotypic ratios that he observed in the F_2 offspring.

From his monohybrid crosses, Mendel developed his first law, the ____________________. This law states that each parent organism has two copies of each discrete unit, or ____________________, and that the two copies separate from each other during ____________________. Mendel then performed dihybrid crosses, and as a result, developed his second law, the ____________________. This law states essentially that the inheritance of one trait does not influence the inheritance of another trait. Mendel's second law applies to genes that are on separate chromosomes or to genes that are so far apart on the same chromosome that they have a strong chance of being separated by ____________________. However, his second law does not apply to genes that exhibit ____________________ because they are close together on the same chromosome.

D. Vector Vocabulary Define the words in the boxes. On the line across each arrow, write a phrase that describes how the words in the boxes are related to each other.

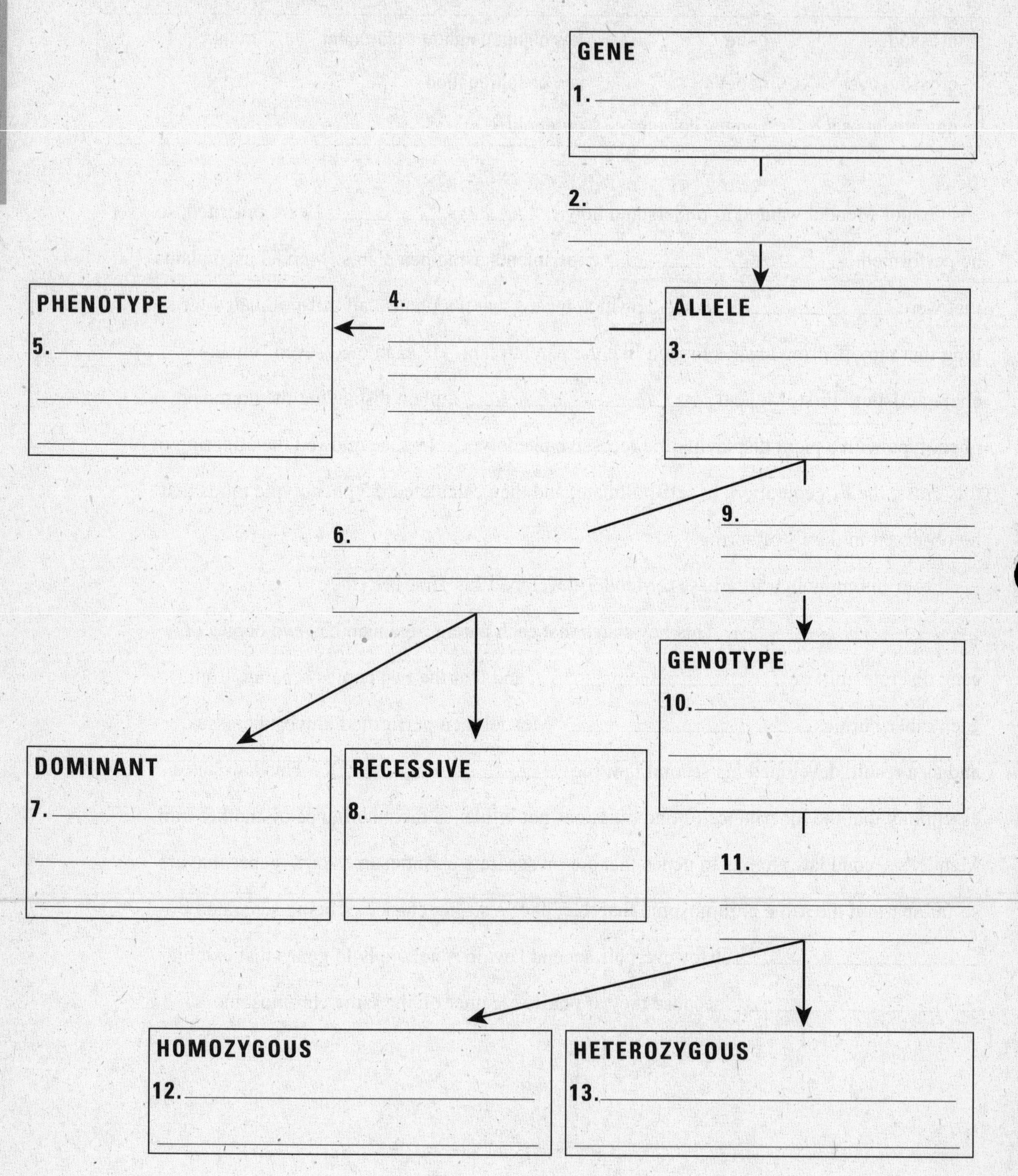

Name Period Date

SECTION **7.1** | CHROMOSOMES AND PHENOTYPE

Study Guide

KEY CONCEPT

The chromosomes on which genes are located can affect the expression of traits.

VOCABULARY
carrier
sex-linked gene
X chromosome inactivation

MAIN IDEA: Two copies of each autosomal gene affect phenotype.

1. What are sex chromosomes?

____

2. What are autosomes?

____

3. How is a carrier different from a person who has a genetic disorder?

____

Complete the two Punnett squares below to compare autosomal recessive disorders with autosomal dominant disorders. Fill in the possible genotypes for offspring, and write in the phenotype (no disorder, carrier, or disorder) for each.

Autosomal Recessive

	D	***d***
D		
d		

Autosomal Dominant

	D	***d***
D		
d		

MAIN IDEA: Males and females can differ in sex-linked traits.

4. What are sex-linked genes?

____

Fill in the Punnett square below to show the pattern of inheritance for sex chromosomes.

Sex Chromosome Inheritance

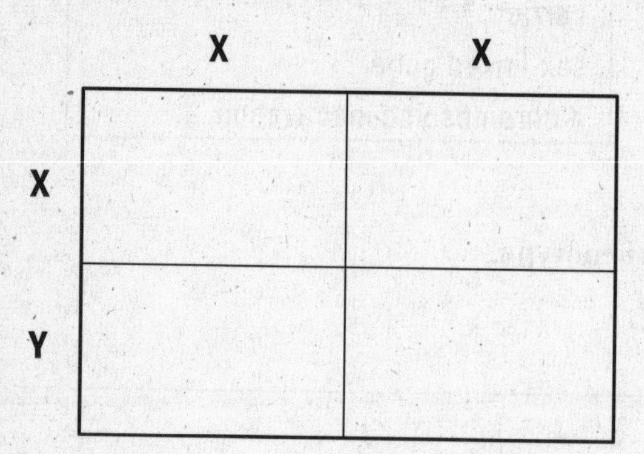

5. In humans, how does a gamete from a male determine the sex of offspring?

____

6. For what are genes on the Y chromosome responsible?

____

7. How are sex-linked genes expressed differently in the phenotypes of males and females?

____

____

Vocabulary Check

8. The verb *carry* means "to transport." How is the everyday meaning of *carry* related to the meaning of the term *carrier* in genetics?

____

9. What is X chromosome inactivation?

____

Name Period Date

SECTION **7.1** | CHROMOSOMES AND PHENOTYPE

Power Notes

Autosomes	**Sex Chromosomes**
Autosomes are:	Sex chromosomes are:
Autosomal gene expression:	Inheritance of sex chromosomes:
Inheritance of autosomes:	Expression of sex-linked genes in males:
	Expression of sex-linked genes in females:

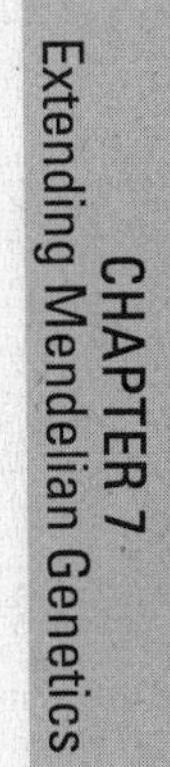

Name Period Date

SECTION **7.1** | CHROMOSOMES AND PHENOTYPE

Reinforcement

KEY CONCEPT The chromosomes on which genes are located can affect the expression of traits.

There are two types of chromosomes: autosomes and sex chromosomes. Genes on the sex chromosomes determine an organism's sex. Autosomes are all of the other chromosomes, and they do not directly affect sex determination. Gene expression can differ depending on the type of chromosome on which a gene is located.

- Autosomal genes: There are two copies of each autosome, which means that there are two copies of each autosomal gene. However, the two copies of a gene may be different alleles. Both copies of a gene can affect phenotype. Much of what has been learned about human genes comes from studies of genetic disorders. Many genetic disorders are caused by recessive alleles on autosomes. People who have one dominant allele and one recessive, disorder-causing allele, do not have the disorder, but can pass it on because they are **carriers** of the disorder.
- Sex-linked genes: Genes on the sex-chromosomes (the X and Y chromosomes in many species) are **sex-linked genes.** In mammals, including humans, and some other animals, XX individuals are female and XY individuals are male. Because males have only one copy of each sex chromosome, all of the genes on each chromosome will be expressed. Expression of sex-linked genes in females is similar to the expression of autosomal genes: two copies of each gene can affect phenotype. However, one X chromosome in each cell is randomly turned off by a process called **X chromosome inactivation.**

1. What is the pattern of expression for autosomal genes?

____

2. What is a carrier?

____

____

3. What are sex-linked genes?

____

4. What are the patterns of expression for sex-linked genes?

____

____

____

Name Period Date

SECTION 7.2 | COMPLEX PATTERNS OF INHERITANCE

Study Guide

KEY CONCEPT

Phenotype is affected by many different factors.

VOCABULARY
incomplete dominance
codominance
polygenic trait

MAIN IDEA: Phenotype can depend on interactions of alleles.

1. How is incomplete dominance different from a dominant and recessive relationship?

____

____

2. How is codominance different from a dominant and recessive relationship?

____

____

3. What is a multiple-allele trait?

____

In the table below, describe how phenotypes appear in incomplete dominance and codominance. Then sketch an example of each.

Interaction	Phenotype	Example
Incomplete dominance	4.	5.
Codominance	6.	7.

Name Period Date

MAIN IDEA: Many genes may interact to produce one trait.
Use the chart below to take notes on polygenic traits and epistasis.

Many genes may interact to produce one trait.

→ Polygenic Traits

→ Epistasis

MAIN IDEA: The environment interacts with genotype.

8. Why is genotype not the only factor that affects phenotype?

____

____

9. List and explain two examples of how environment and genotype can interact.

____

____

Vocabulary Check

10. The prefix *in-* means "not." How is the meaning of this prefix related to the meaning of *incomplete dominance*?

____

11. The prefix *co-* means "together." How is the meaning of this prefix related to the meaning of *codominance*?

____

12. The prefix *poly-* means "many," and the term *genic* means "related to genes." How do these word parts combine to give the meaning of *polygenic*?

____

Name Period Date

SECTION 7.2 | COMPLEX PATTERNS OF INHERITANCE

Power Notes

Complex Patterns of Inheritance

Incomplete dominance:

Codominance:

Multiple alleles:

Polygenic traits:

Epistasis:

Interaction of environment and genotype:

Name Period Date

SECTION 7.2 | COMPLEX PATTERNS OF INHERITANCE

Reinforcement

KEY CONCEPT Phenotype is affected by many different factors.

Although some genetic traits are produced by one gene with dominant and recessive alleles, most genetic traits are the result of more complex relationships among genes and alleles. In many cases phenotype comes from more than just one gene, and many genes have more than just two alleles.

- Incomplete dominance: In incomplete dominance, neither of two alleles is completely dominant or completely recessive. Instead, the alleles show **incomplete dominance,** where the heterozygous phenotype is somewhere between the homozygous dominant and homozygous recessive phenotypes. The heterozygous phenotype is a third, distinct phenotype.
- Codominance: In **codominance,** two alleles of a gene are completely and separately expressed, and both phenotypes are also completely expressed. Human blood type is an example of both codominance and a multiple allele trait. The alleles for blood types A and B are codominant, which can be expressed as an AB blood type. The allele for type O blood is recessive to the other two alleles.
- Polygenic traits: Traits that are produced by two or more genes are **polygenic traits.** Because many different gene interactions can occur with polygenic traits, these traits often have a wide, continuous range of phenotypes.
- Epistasis: An epistatic gene is a gene that can affect the expression of all of the other genes that affect a trait.

The environment can influence gene expression, which then affects phenotype. Human height is a trait that is partially due to environment. Another example is how temperature affects sex determination of sea turtles.

1. What is incomplete dominance?

____

2. What is codominance?

____

3. What is a polygenic trait?

____

4. Describe what happens in epistasis.

____

5. Give an example of how genotype and the environment can interact.

____

Name Period Date

SECTION 7.3 | GENE LINKAGE AND MAPPING

Study Guide

KEY CONCEPT

Genes can be mapped to specific locations on chromosomes.

VOCABULARY
linkage map

MAIN IDEA: Gene linkage was explained through fruit flies.

1. What is gene linkage?

____

2. Why were fruit flies useful in Morgan's research?

____

3. What is the difference between a wild type and a mutant type?

____

4. What did Morgan conclude from his research on fruit flies?

____

____

Complete the sequence below to take notes about the discovery of gene linkage.

Mendel: Genes assort independently of one another.	→	**Punnett, Bateson:**	→	**Morgan:**

MAIN IDEA: Linkage maps estimate distances between genes.

5. How is the distance between two genes related to the chance they are inherited together?

____

6. What hypothesis was the basis of Sturtevant's research?

____

7. What is a linkage map?

____

8. How are cross-over frequencies related to linkage maps?

____

____

9. What do linkage maps show about genes on a chromosome?

____

____

Use the cross-over frequencies given below to draw a linkage map for the four genes listed. Think about the relationship between cross-over frequency and distance in linkage map units. Use Figure 7.11 to help you make the linkage map. Put gene A on the far left of the map, then work through the distances between the gene pairs.

Cross-over Frequencies:		Linkage Map
A-B	20%	
B-C	5%	
A-C	25%	
A-D	7%	
D-B	13%	
D-C	18%	

Name Period Date

SECTION 7.3 | GENE LINKAGE AND MAPPING
Power Notes

Mendel's experiments:

Conclusions:

Punnett and Bateson:

Conclusions:

Morgan:

Conclusions:

Sturtevant's hypothesis:

Sturtevant's experiments:

Making a linkage map:

Name Period Date

SECTION 7.3 | GENE LINKAGE AND MAPPING

Reinforcement

KEY CONCEPT Genes can be mapped to specific locations on chromosomes.

One of Mendel's conclusions from his work on inheritance in pea plants was the law of independent assortment, which stated that genes assort independently of each other during meiosis. However, later experiments suggested that some genes were linked together and did not assort independently. Eventually, research with fruit flies demonstrated that chromosomes, not genes, assort independently and that during meiosis chromosomes could exchange homologous genes.

The chance that two genes on a chromosome will be inherited together is related to the distance between the genes. If two genes are close together, it is very likely that they will be inherited together. If two genes are far apart, it is much more likely that they will be separated by the crossing over that occurs during meiosis. Crossing over takes place when segments of sister chromatids are exchanged.

The frequency of cross-overs is related to the distance between genes on a chromosome. By finding the percentage of times that cross-overs occur from observations of phenotypes in offspring, it is possible to make a map of the locations of the genes. A **linkage map** is a map of the relative locations of genes on a chromosome.

The distance between two genes on a linkage map is expressed in "map units." Two genes that cross over one percent of the time are one map unit apart. Two genes that cross over 20 percent of the time are 20 map units apart. Linkage maps can be made for several different genes at one time if all of their cross-over frequencies are known.

1. How was Mendel's law of independent assortment inaccurate?

____

2. What is the relationship between the distance between two genes and the chance that they will be inherited together?

____

____

____

3. What is a linkage map?

____

4. How are the distances between genes determined for a linkage map?

____

____

Name Period Date

SECTION
7.4

HUMAN GENETICS AND PEDIGREES

Study Guide

KEY CONCEPT

A combination of methods is used to study human genetics.

VOCABULARY
pedigree
karyotype

MAIN IDEA: Human genetics follows the patterns seen in other organisms.

1. How does genetic inheritance follow similar patterns in all sexually reproducing organisms?

2. How are single-gene traits useful in studying human genetics?

MAIN IDEA: Females can carry sex-linked genetic disorders.

3. Who can be carriers of autosomal disorders?

4. Why can females, but not males, be carriers of sex-linked genetic disorders?

MAIN IDEA: A pedigree is a chart for tracing genes in a family.

5. What is a pedigree?

6. How are phenotypes used in pedigree analysis?

7. What information on a pedigree can tell you whether a gene is on an autosome or on a sex chromosome?

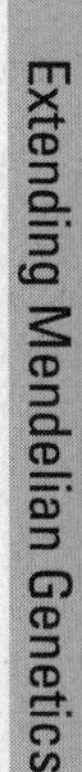

8. Complete the chart to follow the logic necessary to fill out a pedigree for a sex-linked gene. Use X^D and X^d for the dominant and recessive X-linked genes, respectively.

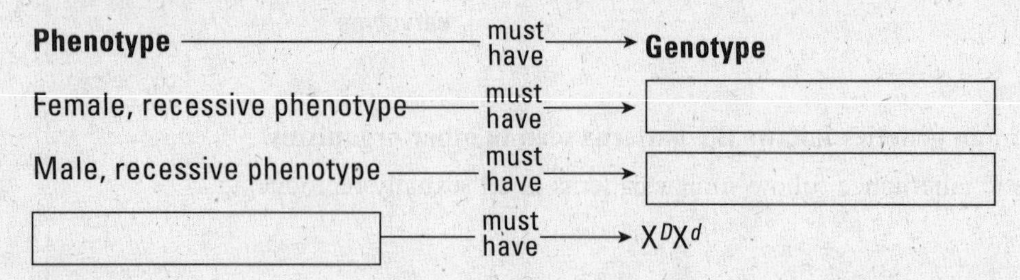

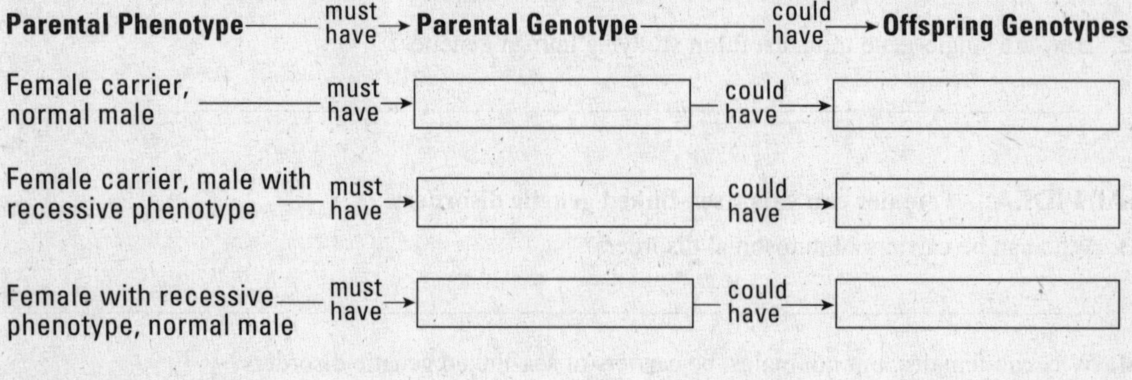

MAIN IDEA: Several methods help map human chromosomes.

9. What are two methods that are used to directly study human chromosomes?

____

10. What does a karyotype show about chromosomes?

____

Vocabulary Check

11. What is a karyotype?

____

Name Period Date

SECTION 7.4 | HUMAN GENETICS AND PEDIGREES

Power Notes

Sex-Linked Disorders	
Males:	Females:

A pedigree chart is:

Tracing Autosomal Genes	Tracing Sex-Linked Genes
• • • •	• • • • •

A karyotype is:

A karyotype shows:

Name Period Date

SECTION 7.4 | HUMAN GENETICS AND PEDIGREES

Reinforcement

KEY CONCEPT A combination of methods is used to study human genetics.

The patterns of inheritance in humans are the same as the patterns of inheritance in other sexually reproducing organisms. Phenotypes are often the result of varying degrees of dominance, several genes, multiple alleles, or sex-linked genes.

Only females can be carriers of sex-linked disorders. Females, who have an XX genotype for their sex chromosomes, must have two recessive alleles to show a recessive phenotype, such as for a recessive sex-linked disorder. Males, on the other hand, have an XY genotype. They will show all of the phenotypes from the genes on their X chromosome, even the recessive alleles, because they cannot have a second, dominant allele that could mask the recessive allele.

The potential for a genetic disorder to be passed on through a family can be studied using pedigree analysis. A **pedigree** is a chart that is used to trace phenotypes and genotypes within a family. It can help show whether someone in a family may have recessive alleles that cause a genetic disorder.

Known phenotypes in a family are used to infer genotypes. Both autosomal genes and sex-linked genes can be traced with pedigrees.

- Tracing autosomal genes: Equal numbers of males and females will have the recessive phenotype. Anyone with the recessive phenotype must be homozygous recessive. Two heterozygous parents can have children who are homozygous dominant, heterozygous, or homozygous recessive.
- Tracing sex-linked genes: More males than females will have the recessive phenotype. Males with a recessive allele will pass it on to all of his daughters. Females can be carriers of a recessive allele and pass it on to either sons or daughters.

In addition to pedigrees, other methods of studying human genetics are used. **Karyotypes,** for example, are pictures of all of a person's chromosomes that can show any large changes in the chromosomes.

1. Why can only females be carriers of sex-linked disorders?

____

____

2. What is a pedigree?

____

3. What is one major difference in pedigrees between autosomal and sex-linked genes?

____

____

CHAPTER 7

CONSTRUCTING BAR GRAPHS

Data Analysis Practice

Bar graphs are used to display data collected during an investigation. Bar graphs are used to compare groups of data that are independent of each other.

The temperature at which sea turtle eggs mature helps determine the sex of the turtles. Evidence suggests that black sea turtle eggs that mature at temperatures below 27.1°C result in all males. In contrast, black sea turtle eggs that mature above 31°C result in all females. Suppose a team of scientists studied the effect of a range of temperatures between those two extremes by incubating different groups of black sea turtle eggs at different temperatures in an incubator. Each group contained 20 eggs. The scientists collected the data shown in the table below.

EFFECT OF TEMPERATURE ON SEA TURTLE SEX DETERMINATION

Incubation Temperature (°C)	Males	Females
27.0	20	0
27.5	18	2
28.0	14	6
28.5	11	9
29.0	12	8
29.5	9	11
30.0	9	11
30.5	4	16
31.0	0	20

1. **Graph** On the next page, construct a bar graph that shows the data in the table. Be sure to include labels on each axis and a title for the graph.

Name Period Date

2. **Analyze** Describe the relationship shown in the graph between incubation temperature and sex determination in sea turtles.

____

____

____

CHAPTER 7 | INCOMPLETE DOMINANCE IN FOUR O'CLOCKS

Pre-AP Activity

In Chapter 7, you have learned that when a homozygous red-flowered four o'clock plant is crossed with a homozygous white-flowered four o'clock plant, the offspring all have pink flowers. This is an example of incomplete dominance, a type of non-Mendelian genetics.

DOMINANCE AT THE MOLECULAR LEVEL

One of the traits Mendel studied in pea plants was flower color. When he crossed a purple-flowered plant, *PP,* with a white-flowered plant, *pp,* all flowers in the first generation of offspring (F_1) had purple flowers. The allele for purple flowers was completely dominant to white flowers.

Each gene holds the genetic information for the production of a particular protein, usually an enzyme. When the dominant allele for purple flower color is present, a series of enzymatic reactions results in the flower cells making a purple pigment. When no dominant allele is present, as in the *pp* homozygous recessive plant, no purple pigment is made, and the flowers are white. The recessive allele most likely codes for an enzyme that is defective and unable to catalyze the reaction that leads to the production of the purple pigment. In the *Pp* heterozygote, only half the amount of pigment is produced, but it is enough to make the flowers purple. The flowers of a *Pp* plant cannot be distinguished from those of a *PP* plant.

INHERITANCE PATTERN OF INCOMPLETE DOMINANCE

Why does the heterozygote four o'clock have pink flowers? The allele for red flower color causes a red pigment, called anthocyanin, to be produced. If only one copy of the allele is present, only half the amount of red pigment is made, which effectively dilutes the coloring so that the flowers appear pink, not red.

Red four o'clock R_1R_1

White four o'clock R_1R_1		R_1	R_1
	R_2	R_1R_2 Pink	R_1R_2 Pink
	R_2	R_1R_2 Pink	R_1R_2 Pink

F_1 generation: four pink four o'clocks

What is the inheritance pattern of a trait that is controlled by incomplete dominance? To find out, you will diagram the self-fertilization of one heterozygous F_1 plant and then the self-fertilization of all the resulting genotypes of the F_2 generation.

Name Period Date

1. In the Punnett squares below, diagram the self-fertilization, a self-cross, of one pink-flowered F_1 heterozygous plant (R_1R_2). Then use the second series of Punnett squares to diagram the self-fertilization of each genotype of the F_2 generation. Include both the genotype and phenotype in the cells of the Punnett Square. If you have colored pencils available, you can color in the squares with the appropriate flower colors.

F_1 self-cross

F_2 self-crosses

2. Describe the pattern of inheritance for incomplete dominance.

___

___

___

3. As described in Chapter 6, Mendel's work with pea plants demonstrated that the factors that control heritable traits exist as discrete units, what we now call genes. Yet the cross of a red four o'clock plant with a white four o'clock clearly shows a blend in the phenotype: red plus white equals pink. How are the Punnett squares you completed evidence that heritable factors are discrete units, despite the blending of colors?

___

___

___

___

___

___

___

CHAPTER 7 | ROYAL HEMOPHILIA

Pre-AP Activity

In Chapter 7, you have learned how sex-linked traits are inherited, and how to analyze a pedigree. You also learned how to make and analyze a pedigree. Hemophilia, a condition that results in excessive bleeding after injury due to an abnormal blood clotting factor, is a sex-linked trait. By analyzing a pedigree of Queen Victoria's family, you will learn more about this genetic disorder.

QUEEN VICTORIA'S FAMILY

The most famous example of hemophilia occurred in the family of Victoria, Queen of England from 1837 to 1901. She was England's longest reigning monarch.

Victoria married her cousin, Prince Albert, and they had nine children—five girls and four boys. As you can see in the pedigree on the next page, three of her children inherited the allele for hemophilia. Because it was common for members of European royal families to marry into other royal families, the defective allele was carried into the royal families of Russia, Germany, and Spain. The disease has been called the royal disease, or royal hemophilia. Ten of Victoria's male descendants had hemophilia.

Answer the following questions on a separate sheet of paper.

1. Victoria's youngest child, Beatrice, had one daughter, one normal son, and two sons with hemophilia. Beatrice's daughter, Eugenie, married King Alfonso XIII of Spain. They had six children, one of whom was the father of Juan Carlos, the current King of Spain. What is Juan Carlos's phenotype—normal, carrier, or hemophilic? Explain.

2. Victoria's daughter Alice had a daughter, Alix, who carried the defective allele into the royal Russian family when she married Tsar Nicholas II. They had four daughters and one son, Alexis. Alexis had hemophilia. The entire family was murdered during the Russian Revolution. What is the probability that one of Alexis's sisters was a carrier? What is the probability that all four of Alexis's sisters were carriers? Explain.

3. If Alexis had lived and married a normal woman, what is the probability that he would have had a daughter with hemophilia? Explain.

4. Is it possible for a female to have hemophilia? Explain.

5. What is the probability that the next generation of the present British royal family—Charles, Andrew, Edward, and Ann—will have hemophilia? Explain.

Name Period Date

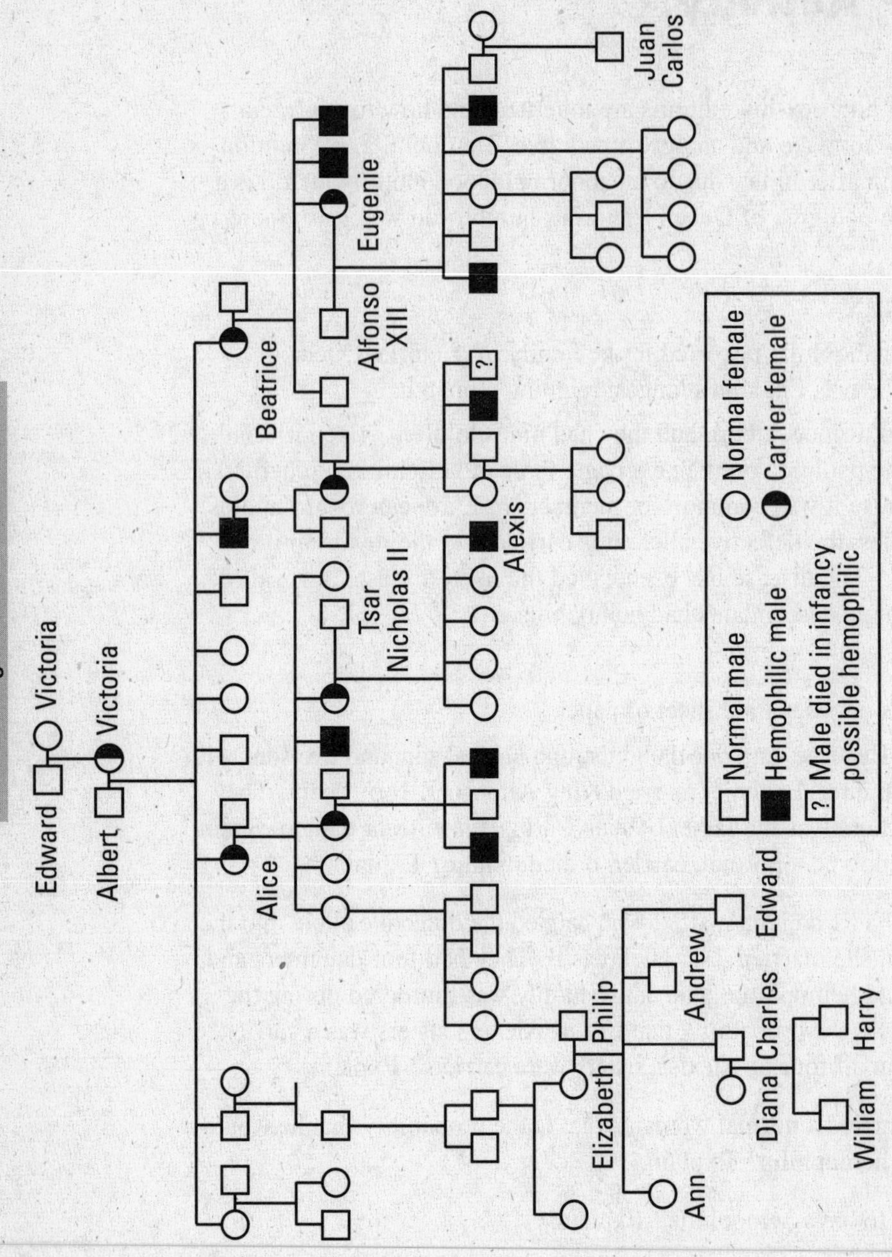

Name Period Date

CHAPTER 7

EXTENDING MENDELIAN GENETICS

Vocabulary Practice

carrier	incomplete dominance	linkage map
sex-linked gene	codominance	pedigree
X chromosome inactivation	polygenic trait	karyotype

A. Compound Word Puzzle Read the phrase and write the word that it most closely describes. Then write another phrase that describes the same word in a different way.

PHRASE 1	WORD	PHRASE 2
picture of all human chromosomes	**Example** karyotype	can show large changes in chromosomes
genes located on the sex chromosomes	**1.**	
it shows the relative locations of genes on a chromosome	**2.**	
one X chromosome is randomly turned off	**3.**	
a chart that is used to trace phenotypes and genotypes in a family	**4.**	
many genes interact to produce a single trait	**5.**	
an "in-between" phenotype	**6.**	

B. Words in Context Answer the questions to show your understanding of the vocabulary words.

1. Which is like a **karyotype,** a satellite weather map, or the temperature on one street corner?

____

2. Is **incomplete dominance** like a glass of cranberry-raspberry juice or a pizza with everything?

____

3. Is **X chromosome inactivation** like an electrical generator or a power failure?

____

4. Would a **pedigree** be used to trace genes in a family or to send a dog to obedience school?

____

5. Is **codominance** like doing your homework or two people talking at the same time?

____

6. Which is like a **carrier,** a ferry crossing a lake, or a door opening?

____

7. Are exact directions or a general idea of where you are going more like a **linkage map?**

____

8. Is a **polygenic trait** more like a basketball team or a figure skater?

____

C. Do-It Yourself Matching In a random order, write short definitions for each term on the blank lines to the right. Then give your paper to a classmate who should write the number of the term next to the correct definition.

1. sex-linked gene ____ _______________
2. incomplete dominance ____ _______________
3. carrier ____ _______________
4. linkage map ____ _______________
5. codominance ____ _______________
6. karyotype ____ _______________

Name Period Date

D. Who Am I? Choose among these terms to answer the riddles below:

carrier	karyotype	polygenic trait
codominance	linkage map	X chromosome inactivation
incomplete dominance	pedigree	

1. I am the process that randomly turns off one X chromosome in a human female's cells. ______
2. I am an interaction between two alleles in which both alleles are fully and separately expressed. ______
3. I am a chart that can be used to trace genes through a family. ______
4. I am a picture that shows the overall structure of chromosomes. ______
5. I am an interaction between two alleles that produces a phenotype that is between the phenotypes of homozygotes. ______
6. I am a person who does not show a genetic disorder, but I can pass it on to my offspring. ______
7. I am a map of genes on a chromosome, but I do not show the exact locations of the genes. ______
8. I am a trait that is the result of many genes. ______

E. Find the Odd Word Put a checkmark next to the word that does not belong.

1. ____ karyotype
   ____ linkage map
   ____ X chromosome inactivation

   Explanation ______

2. ____ sex-linked gene
   ____ polygenic trait
   ____ carrier

   Explanation ______

VOCABULARY PRACTICE, CONTINUED

3. _____ linkage map Explanation_____________________

_____ incomplete dominance _____________________

_____ codominance

4. _____ incomplete dominance Explanation_____________________

_____ karyotype _____________________

_____ pedigree

F. Analogies Read each analogy. Decide which term is most like it.

carrier	codominance	linkage map
X chromosome inactivation	polygenic trait	karyotype
incomplete dominance		

1. Airport baggage handler _____________________

2. Blending the ingredients of a fruit smoothie _____________________

3. Randomly flipping switches in an electrical panel _____________________

4. A still-life painting _____________________

5. All of the people who make up the United States _____________________

6. Mixing the ingredients of a fruit salad _____________________

7. A train schedule that shows the stops made by the train _____________________

Write your own analogies to show the meaning of these terms:

8. sex-linked gene _____________________

____

____

9. pedigree _____________________

____

____

Name Period Date

SECTION 8.1 | IDENTIFYING DNA AS THE GENETIC MATERIAL

Study Guide

KEY CONCEPT

DNA was identified as the genetic material through a series of experiments.

VOCABULARY
bacteriophage

MAIN IDEA: Griffith finds a "transforming principle."

Write the results of Griffith's experiments in the boxes below.

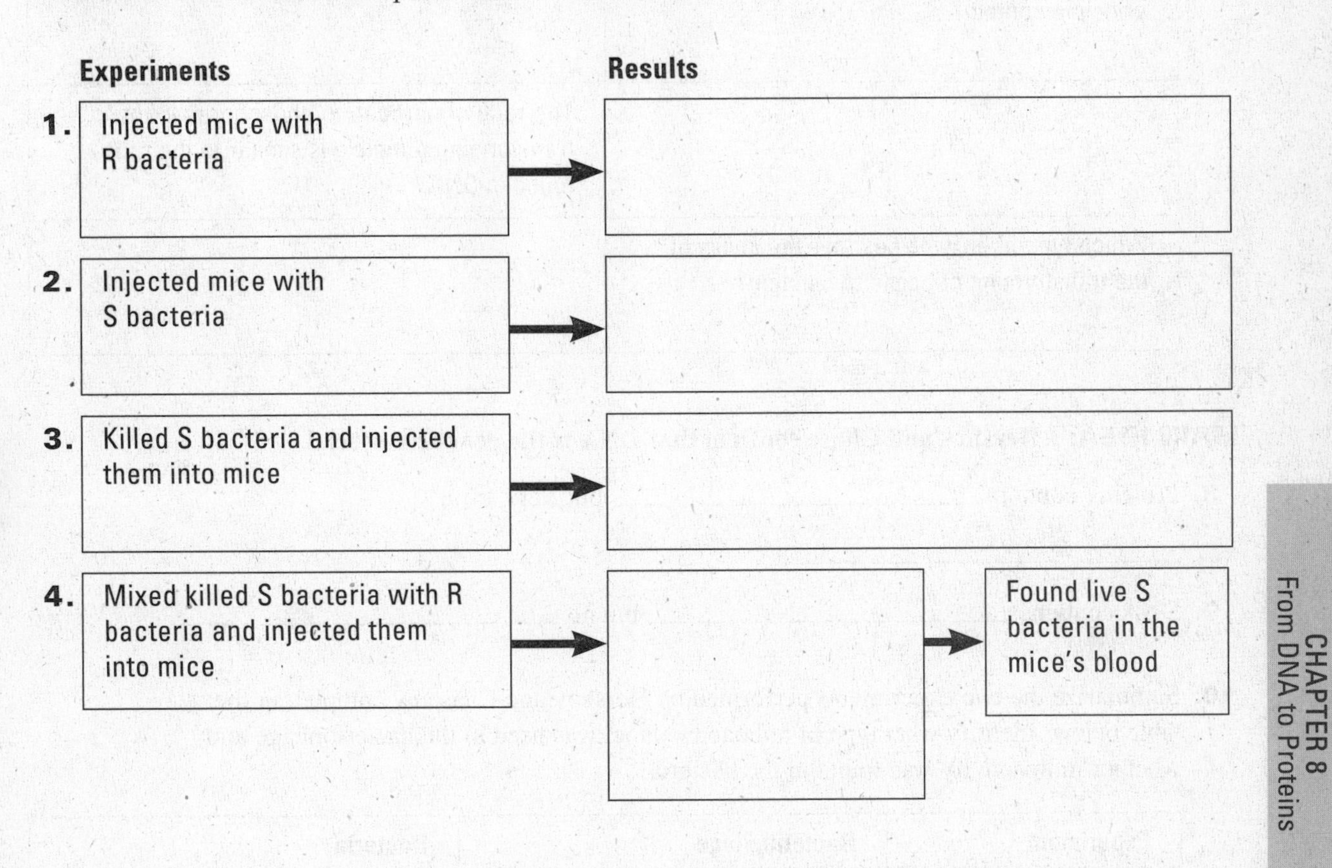

5. Which type of bacteria caused disease, the S form or the R form?

____

6. What conclusions did Griffith make based on his experimental results?

____

____

CHAPTER 8
From DNA to Proteins

MAIN IDEA: Avery identifies DNA as the transforming principle.

7. Avery and his team isolated Griffith's transforming principle and performed three tests to learn if it was DNA or protein. In the table below, summarize Avery's work by writing the question he was asking or the results of his experiment.

Avery's Question	Results
What type of molecule does the transforming principle contain?	
	The ratio of nitrogen to phosphorus in the transforming principle is similar to the ratio found in DNA.
Which type of enzyme destroys the ability of the transforming principle to function?	

MAIN IDEA: Hershey and Chase confirm that DNA is the genetic material.

8. Proteins contain ______________ but very little ______________.

9. DNA contains ______________ but no ______________.

10. Summarize the two experiments performed by Hershey and Chase by completing the table below. Identify what type of radioactive label was used in the bacteriophage and whether radioactivity was found in the bacteria.

Experiment	Bacteriophage	Bacteria
Experiment 1		
Experiment 2		

Vocabulary Check

11. Explain what a bacteriophage is and describe or sketch its structure.

____

Name Period Date

SECTION 8.1 | IDENTIFYING DNA AS THE GENETIC MATERIAL

Power Notes

Griffith's experiments:

Conclusion:

Avery's experiments:

-
-
-

Conclusion:

Hershey and Chase's experiments:

-
-

Conclusion:

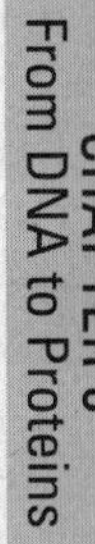

Name Period Date

SECTION 8.1 | IDENTIFYING DNA AS THE GENETIC MATERIAL

Reinforcement

KEY CONCEPT DNA was identified as the genetic material through a series of experiments.

A series of experiments helped scientists recognize that DNA is the genetic material. One of the earliest was done by Frederick Griffith who was studying two forms of the bacterium that causes pneumonia. The S form was surrounded by a coating that made them look smooth. The R form did not have a coating, and the colonies looked rough. Griffith injected these bacteria into mice and found that only the S type killed the mice. When the S bacteria were killed, they did not cause the mice to die. However, when killed S bacteria were mixed with live R bacteria, the mice died and Griffith found live S bacteria in their blood. This led Griffith to conclude that there was a transforming principle that could change R bacteria into S bacteria.

Oswald Avery, another scientist, developed a way to purify this transforming principle. He then conducted a series of chemical tests to find out what it was. Many scientists thought that DNA was too simple of a molecule to be the genetic material and that proteins, being more complex, were a better candidate. However, Avery made three key discoveries about his samples of transforming principle that showed otherwise:

- DNA was present, not protein.
- The chemical composition matched that of DNA, not protein.
- The addition of enzymes that break down DNA made the transforming principle inactive. The addition of enzymes that break down proteins or RNA had no effect.

Alfred Hershey and Martha Chase carried out the final, conclusive experiments in 1952. **Bacteriophages** are viruses that infect bacteria and take over bacteria's genetic machinery to make more viruses. They consist of a protein coat surrounding DNA. Hershey and Chase grew these viruses in cultures containing radioactively labeled sulfur, a component of proteins, or phosphorus, a component of DNA. Bacteria were then infected with viruses that either had radioactively labeled sulfur or phosphorous. Hershey and Chase next separated the viruses from the bacteria with a blender. The bacteria had radioactive phosphorus but no radioactive sulfur. Hershey and Chase concluded that the viruses' DNA, but not the protein coat, had entered the bacteria.

1. What was "transformed" in Griffith's experiment?

____

____

2. Which molecule had entered the bacterium in the Hershey-Chase experiments, sulfur or phosphorus? Which molecule is a major component of DNA?

____

Name Period Date

SECTION
8.2

STRUCTURE OF DNA
Study Guide

KEY CONCEPT
DNA structure is the same in all organisms.

VOCABULARY	
nucleotide	base pairing rules
double helix	

MAIN IDEA: DNA is composed of four types of nucleotides.
In the space below, draw a nucleotide and label its three parts using words and arrows.

1. How many types of nucleotides are present in DNA?

2. Which parts are the same in all nucleotides? Which part is different?

MAIN IDEA: Watson and Crick developed an accurate model of DNA's three-dimensional structure.

3. What did Franklin's data reveal about the structure of DNA?

4. How did Watson and Crick determine the three-dimensional shape of DNA?

5. How does DNA base pairing result in a molecule that has a uniform width?

____

MAIN IDEA: Nucleotides always pair in the same way.

6. What nucleotide pairs with T? with C?

____

In the space below, draw a DNA double helix. Label the sugar-phosphate backbone, the nitrogen-containing bases, and the hydrogen bonds.

Vocabulary Check

7. Explain how the DNA double helix is similar to a spiral staircase.

____

____

8. How do the base pairing rules relate to Chargaff's rules?

____

____

Name Period Date

SECTION 8.2 | STRUCTURE OF DNA

Power Notes

Parts of a DNA molecule

Overall shape:

Nitrogen-containing bases

Backbone

1.

2.

Pyrimidines

Purines

Base pairing rules:

Bonding

1.

2.

Chargaff's rules:

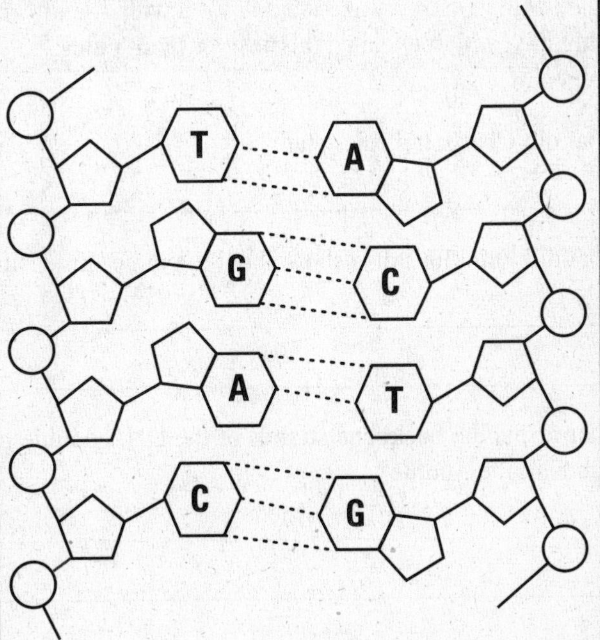

CHAPTER 8
From DNA to Proteins

Name Period Date

SECTION **8.2** | STRUCTURE OF DNA

Reinforcement

KEY CONCEPT DNA structure is the same in all organisms.

DNA is a chain of nucleotides. In DNA, each **nucleotide** is made of a phosphate group, a sugar called deoxyribose, and one of four nitrogen-containing bases. These four bases are cytosine (C), thymine (T), adenine (A), and guanine (G). Two of the bases, C and T, have a single-ring structure. The other two bases, A and G, have a double-ring structure.

Although scientists had a good understanding of the chemical structure of DNA by the 1950s, they did not understand its three-dimensional structure. The contributions of several scientists helped lead to this important discovery.

- Erwin Chargaff analyzed the DNA from many different organisms and realized that the amount of A is equal to the amount of T, and the amount of C is equal to the amount of G. This A = T and C = G relationship became known as Chargaff's rules.
- Rosalind Franklin and Maurice Wilkins studied DNA structure using x-ray crystallography. Franklin's data suggested that DNA is a helix consisting of two strands that are a regular, consistent width apart.

James Watson and Francis Crick applied Franklin's and Chargaff's data in building a three-dimensional model of DNA. They confirmed that DNA is a **double helix** in which two strands of DNA wind around each other like a twisted ladder. The sugar and phosphate molecules form the outside strands of the helix, and the bases pair together in the middle, forming hydrogen bonds that hold the two sides of the helix together. A base with a double ring pairs with a base with a single ring. Thus, in accordance with Chargaff's rules, they realized that A pairs with T, and C pairs with G. The bases always pair this way, which is called the **base pairing rules.**

1. What did Chargaff's rules state?

____

2. What did Franklin's data show about the three-dimensional structure of DNA?

____

____

3. What forms the backbone strands of the DNA double helix? What connects these strands in the middle?

____

____

Name Period Date

SECTION 8.3 | DNA REPLICATION
Study Guide

KEY CONCEPT
DNA replication copies the genetic information of a cell.

VOCABULARY	
replication	DNA polymerase

MAIN IDEA: Replication copies the genetic information.

1. What is DNA replication?

2. Where does DNA replication take place in a eukaryotic cell?

3. When is DNA replicated during the cell cycle?

4. Why does DNA replication need to occur?

5. What is a template?

6. If one strand of DNA had the sequence TAGGTAC, what would be the sequence of the complementary DNA strand?

MAIN IDEA: Proteins carry out the process of replication.

7. What roles do proteins play in DNA replication?

8. What must be broken for the DNA strand to separate?

9. Why is DNA replication called semiconservative?

Name Period Date

Use words and diagrams to summarize the steps of replication, in order, in the boxes below.

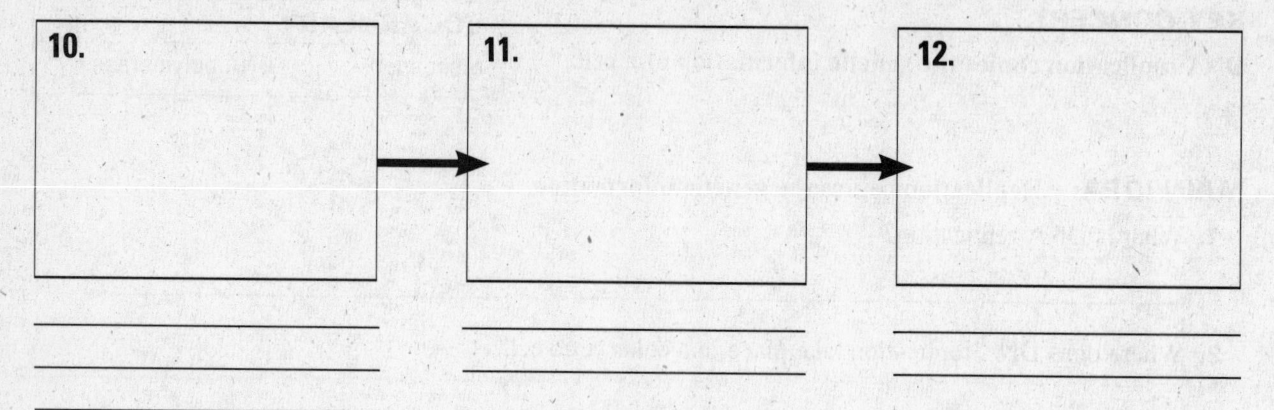

MAIN IDEA: Replication is fast and accurate.

13. Human chromosomes have hundreds of ________________, where the DNA is unzipped so replication can begin.

14. DNA polymerase has a ________________ function that enables it to detect errors and correct them.

Vocabulary Check

15. Explain what DNA polymerase is by breaking the word into its parts.

____

16. Write a short analogy to explain what replication is.

____

Be Creative

17. People sometimes like to display bumper stickers that relate to their trade or field of study. For example, a chemist may have a bumper sticker that says "It takes alkynes to make the world." Then, chemists or other people who know that an alkyne is a molecule that contains carbon atoms joined by a triple bond get a nice little chuckle out of the play on words. Use your knowledge of DNA replication to write a bumper sticker.

____

____

Name Period Date

SECTION 8.3 | DNA REPLICATION

Power Notes

General description:

Process

1.

2.

3.

End result

4.

Identify the structures.

1. ______

2. ______

3. ______

4. ______

Name Period Date

SECTION 8.3 | DNA REPLICATION
Reinforcement

KEY CONCEPT DNA replication copies the genetic information of a cell.

Every cell needs its own complete set of DNA, and the discovery of the three-dimensional structure of DNA immediately suggested a mechanism by which the copying of DNA, or DNA **replication,** could occur. Because the DNA bases pair in only one way, both strands of DNA act as templates that direct the production of a new, complementary strand. DNA replication takes place during the S stage of the cell cycle.

The process of DNA replication is very similar in both eukaryotes and prokaryotes, but we will focus on eukaryotes.

- During the S stage of the cell cycle, the DNA is loosely organized in the nucleus. Certain enzymes start to unzip the double helix at places called origins of replication. The double helix unzips in both directions along the strand. Eukaryotic chromosomes are very long, so they have many origins of replication to help speed the process. Other proteins hold the two strands apart.
- The unzipping exposes the bases on the DNA strands and enables free-floating nucleotides to pair up with their complementary bases. **DNA polymerases** bond the nucleotides together to form new strands that are complementary to the original template strands.
- The result is two identical strands of DNA. DNA replication is described as semiconservative because each DNA molecule has one new strand and one original strand.

DNA polymerase not only bonds nucleotides together. It also has a proofreading function. It can detect incorrectly paired nucleotides, clip them out, and replace them with the correct nucleotides. Uncorrected errors are limited to about one per 1 billion nucleotides.

1. Why is DNA replication described as semiconservative?

____

____

2. What are two major functions that DNA polymerase performs?

____

____

Name Period Date

SECTION **8.4** | TRANSCRIPTION

Study Guide

KEY CONCEPT

Transcription converts a gene into a single-stranded RNA molecule.

VOCABULARY	
central dogma	messenger RNA (mRNA)
RNA	ribosomal RNA (rRNA)
transcription	transfer RNA (tRNA)
RNA polymerase	

MAIN IDEA: RNA carries DNA's instructions.

Label each of the processes represented by the arrows in the diagram below. Write where each of these processes takes place in a eukaryotic cell in parentheses.

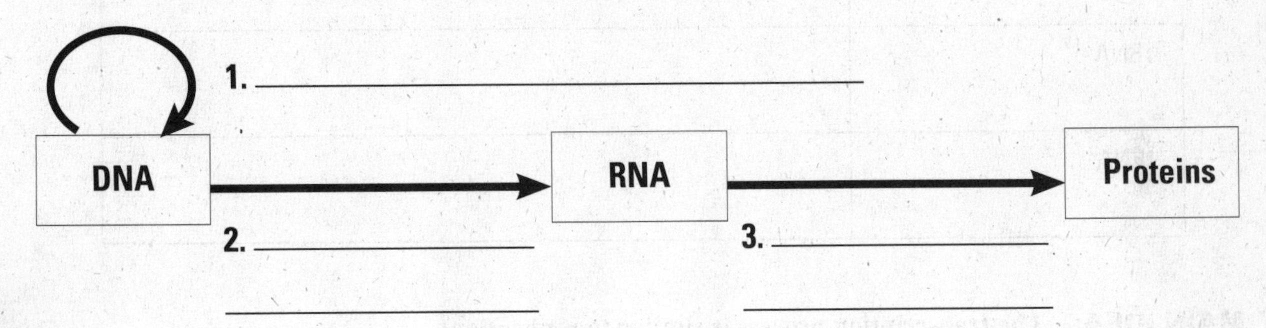

Fill in the table below to contrast DNA and RNA.

DNA	RNA
4. Contains the sugar deoxyribose	
5.	Has the bases A, C, G, and U
6. Typically double-stranded	

MAIN IDEA: Transcription makes three types of RNA.

7. What enzyme helps a cell to make a strand of RNA?

____

CHAPTER 8 From DNA to Proteins

STUDY GUIDE, CONTINUED

8. Summarize the three key steps of transcription.

9. Write the basic function of each type of RNA in the chart below.

Type of RNA	Function
mRNA	
rRNA	
tRNA	

MAIN IDEA: The transcription process is similar to replication.

10. List two ways that the processes of transcription and replication are similar.

11. List two ways that the end results of transcription and replication differ.

Vocabulary Check

12. How does the name of each type of RNA tell what it does?

13. What is transcription?

Name Period Date

SECTION 8.4 | TRANSCRIPTION

Power Notes

Central Dogma

1. DNA	2. →	3.	4. →	5.

DNA:	RNA:
• • •	• • •

Transcription

Label the parts on the lines below. Summarize the steps of transcription in the boxes.

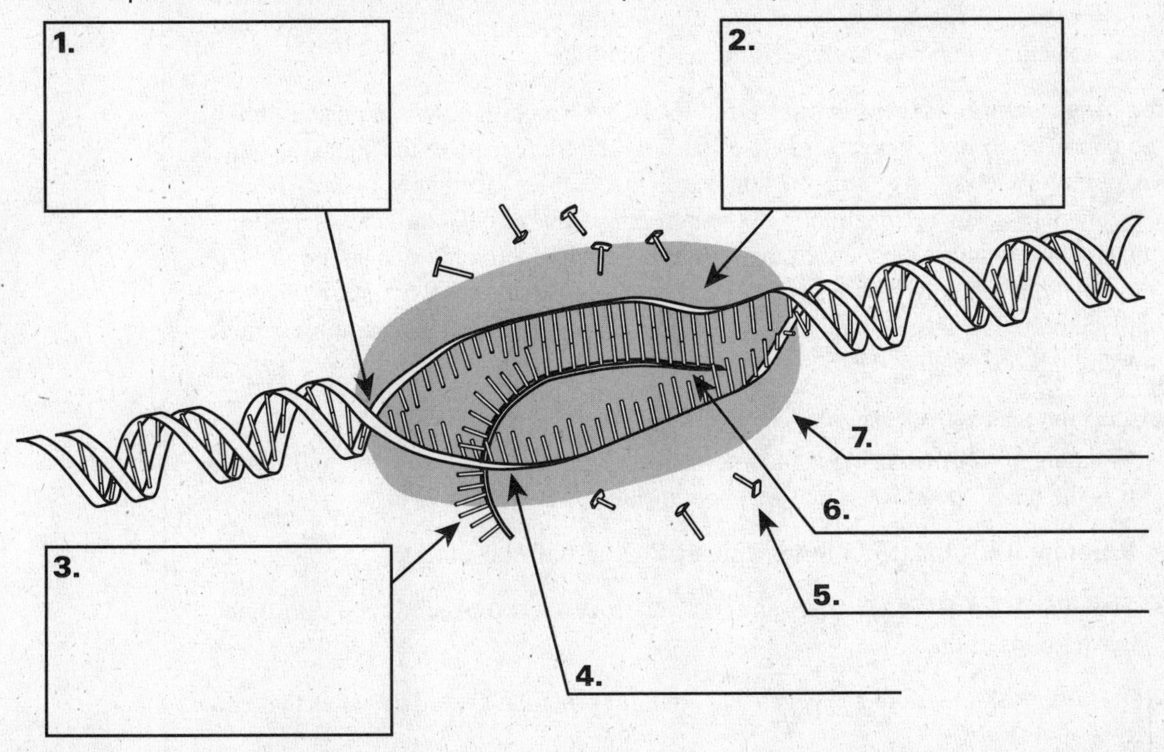

RNA Type	Function
1. Messenger RNA (mRNA)	
2.	
3.	

CHAPTER 8 From DNA to Proteins

Name Period Date

SECTION **8.4** TRANSCRIPTION

Reinforcement

KEY CONCEPT Transcription converts a gene into a single-stranded RNA molecule.

DNA provides the instructions needed by a cell to make proteins. But the instructions are not made directly into proteins. First, a DNA message is converted into RNA in a process called transcription. Then, the RNA message is converted into proteins in a process called translation. The relationship between these molecules and processes is summed up in the **central dogma,** which states that information flows in one direction, from DNA to RNA to proteins.

Like DNA, **RNA** is a nucleic acid. It is made of nucleotides that consist of a phosphate group, a sugar, and a nitrogen-containing base. However, RNA differs in important ways from DNA: (1) RNA contains the sugar ribose, not deoxyribose; (2) RNA is made up of the nucleotides A, C, G, and uracil, U, which forms base pairs with A; (3) RNA is usually single-stranded. This single-stranded structure enables RNA to fold back on itself into specific structures that can catalyze reactions, much like an enzyme.

During **transcription,** a gene is transferred into RNA. Specific DNA sequences and a combination of accessory proteins help RNA polymerase recognize the start of a gene. **RNA polymerase** is a large enzyme that bonds nucleotides together to make RNA. RNA polymerase, in combination with the other proteins, forms a large transcription complex that unwinds a segment of the DNA molecule. Using only one strand of DNA as a template, RNA polymerase strings together a complementary RNA strand that has U in place of T. The DNA strand zips back together as the transcription complex moves forward along the gene.

Transcription makes three main types of RNA.

- **Messenger RNA (mRNA)** is the intermediate message between DNA and proteins. It is the only type of RNA that will be translated to form a protein.
- **Ribosomal RNA (rRNA)** forms a significant part of ribosomes.
- **Transfer RNA (tRNA)** carries amino acids from the cytoplasm to the ribosome during translation.

The DNA of a cell therefore has genes that code for proteins, as well as genes that code for rRNA and tRNA.

1. What is stated in the central dogma?

____

2. What are the three main types of RNA? Which is translated into a protein?

____

Name Period Date

SECTION 8.5 | TRANSLATION

Study Guide

KEY CONCEPT

Translation converts an mRNA message into a polypeptide, or protein.

VOCABULARY		
translation	stop codon	anticodon
codon	start codon	

MAIN IDEA: Amino acids are coded by mRNA base sequences.

1. What is translation?

____

2. What is a codon?

____

3. Would the codons in Figure 8.13 be found in a strand of DNA or RNA?

____

4. What is a reading frame?

____

Refer to Figure 8.13 to complete the table below.

Codon	Amino Acid or Function
5. AGA	
6. UAG	
7.	tryptophan (Trp)
8. GGA	

MAIN IDEA: Amino acids are linked to become a protein.

9. ______________ and ______________ are the tools that help a cell translate an mRNA message into a polypeptide.

10. The ______________ subunit of a ribosome holds onto the mRNA strand.

11. The ______________ subunit of a ribosome has binding sites for tRNA.

CHAPTER 8 From DNA to Proteins

12. A tRNA molecule is attached to an ________________ at one end and has an ________________ at the other end.

Fill in the cycle diagram below to outline the steps of translation.

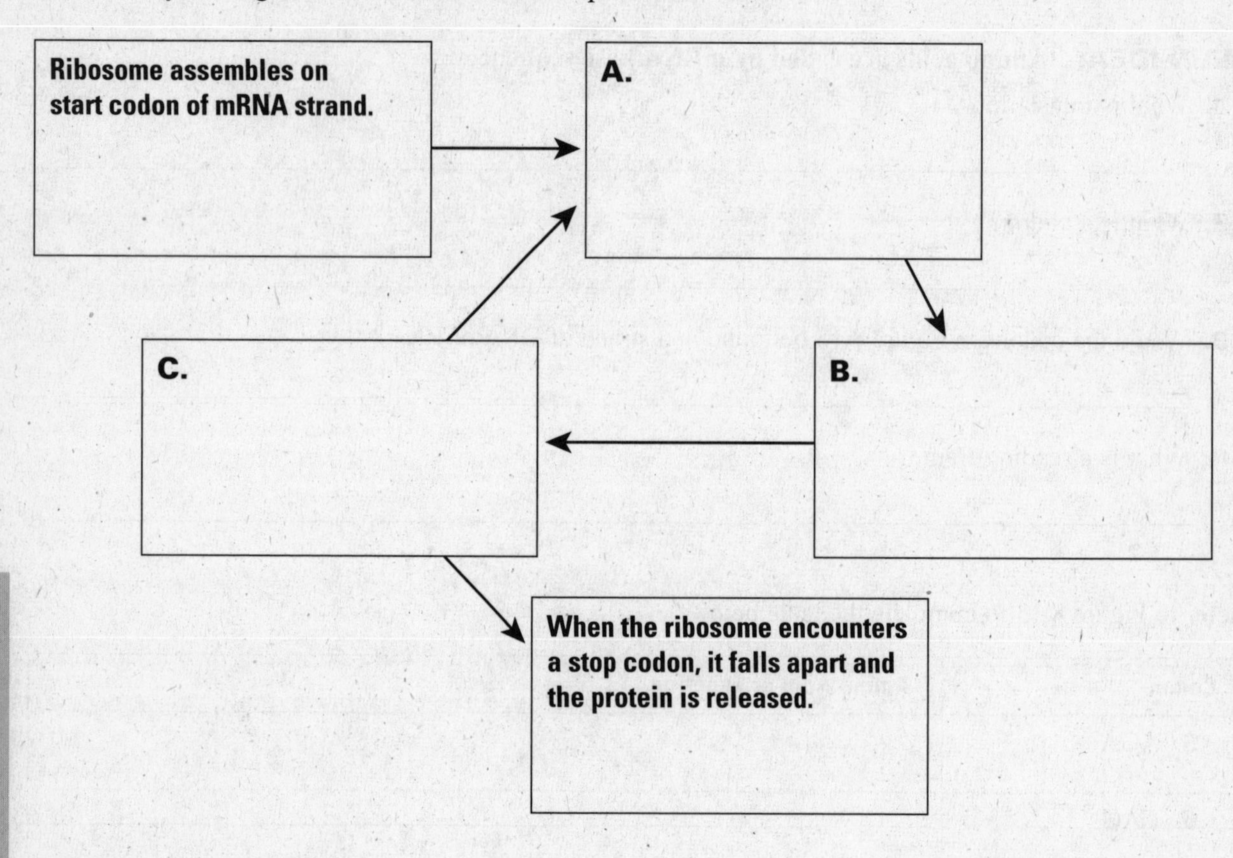

Vocabulary Check

13. What are AGG, GCA, and GUU examples of?

____

14. What is a set of three nucleotides on a tRNA molecule that is complementary to an mRNA codon?

____

15. What do codons code for in addition to amino acids?

____

Name Period Date

SECTION 8.5

TRANSLATION
Power Notes

Triplet Code

Reading frame:

Common language:

Codon

Start codon:

Stop codon:

Ribosome
•
•

Anticodon

Transfer RNA (tRNA)

Translation

Parts

1.

2.

4.

3.

Met

Leu

Cys

8.

7.

6.

5.

Process

1.

2.

3.

Name Period Date

SECTION
8.5

TRANSLATION
Reinforcement

KEY CONCEPT Translation converts an mRNA message into a polypeptide, or protein.

Translation is the process that converts an mRNA message into a polypeptide, or protein. An mRNA message is made up of combinations of four nucleotides, whereas proteins are made up of twenty types of amino acids. The mRNA message is read as a series of non-overlapping **codons,** a sequence of three nucleotides that code for an amino acid. Many amino acids are coded for by more than one codon. In general, codons that code for the same amino acid share the same first two nucleotides. Three codons, called **stop codons,** signal the end of the polypeptide. There is also a **start codon,** which both signals the start of translation and codes for the amino acid methionine. This genetic code is the same in almost all organisms, so it is sometimes called the universal genetic code.

Although tRNA and rRNA are not translated into proteins, they play key roles in helping cells translate mRNA into proteins. Each tRNA molecule folds up into a characteristic L shape. One end has three nucleotides called an **anticodon,** which recognize and bind to a codon on the mRNA strand. The other end of the tRNA molecule carries a specific amino acid. A combination of rRNA and proteins make up the ribosome. Ribosomes consist of a large and small subunit. The large subunit has binding sites for tRNA. The small subunit binds to the mRNA strand.

At the start of translation, a small subunit binds to an mRNA strand. Then the large subunit joins. A tRNA molecule binds to the start codon. Another tRNA molecule binds to the next codon. The ribosome forms a bond between the two amino acids carried by the tRNA molecules and pulls the mRNA strand by the length of one codon. This causes the first tRNA molecule to be released and opens up a new codon for binding. This process continues to be repeated until a stop codon is reached and the ribosome falls apart.

1. What is a codon?

____

____

2. What role does tRNA play in translation?

____

____

3. What forms the bond between neighboring amino acids?

____

Name Period Date

SECTION 8.6 | GENE EXPRESSION AND REGULATION

Study Guide

KEY CONCEPT

Gene expression is carefully regulated in both prokaryotic and eukaryotic cells.

VOCABULARY	
promoter	exon
operon	intron

MAIN IDEA: Prokaryotic cells turn genes on and off by controlling transcription.

1. Why is gene expression regulated in prokaryotic cells?

____

2. In prokaryotic cells, gene expression is typically regulated at the start of _______________.

3. A _______________ is a segment of DNA that helps RNA polymerase recognize the start of a gene.

4. An _______________ is a region of DNA that includes a _______________, an _______________, and one or more _______________ that code for proteins needed to carry out a task.

Complete the cause-and-effect diagram below about the *lac* operon.

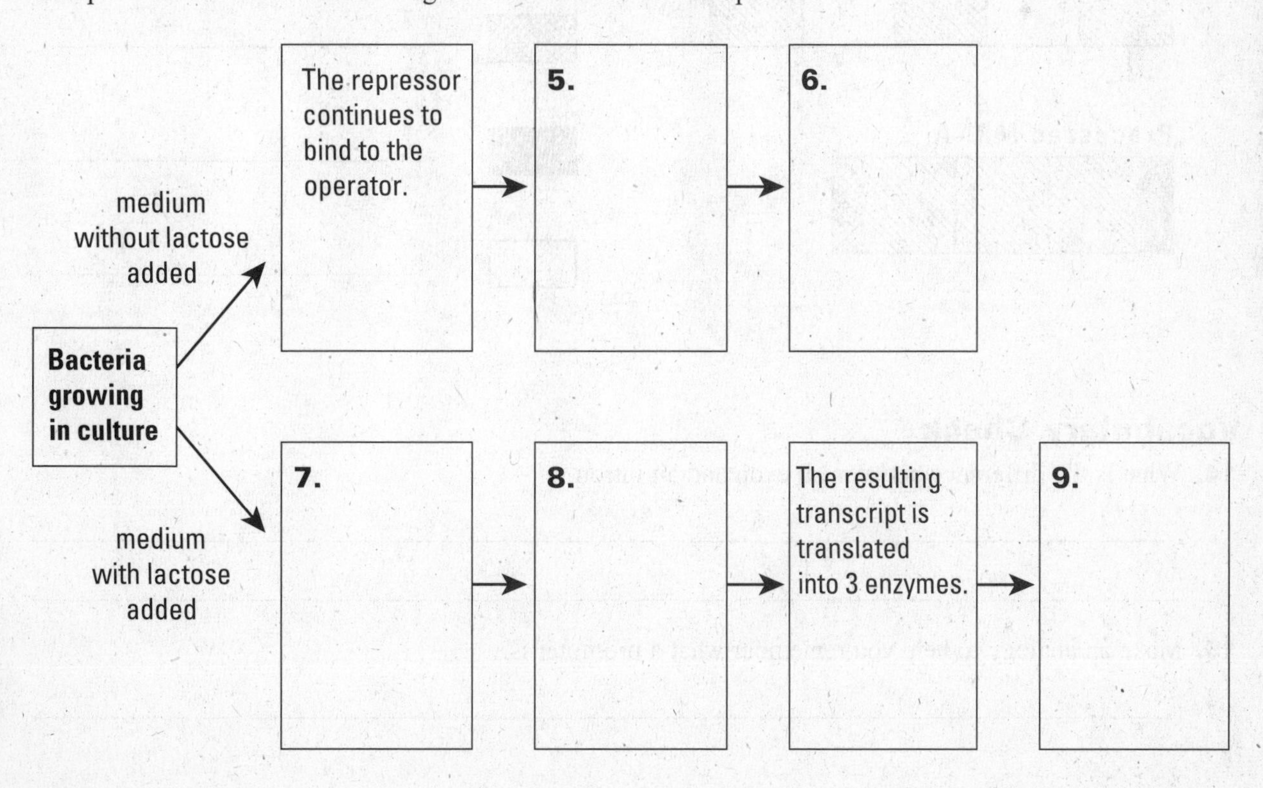

Name Period Date

MAIN IDEA: Eukaryotic cells regulate gene expression at many points.

10. Why do the cells in your body differ from each other?

____

11. What role do transcription factors play in a cell?

____

12. What is a TATA box?

____

13. What is "sonic hedgehog" an example of?

____

MAIN IDEA: The diagrams below represent unprocessed and processed mRNA in a eukaryotic cell. Using the diagrams as a reference, fill in the legend with the corresponding element: cap, exon, intron, tail.

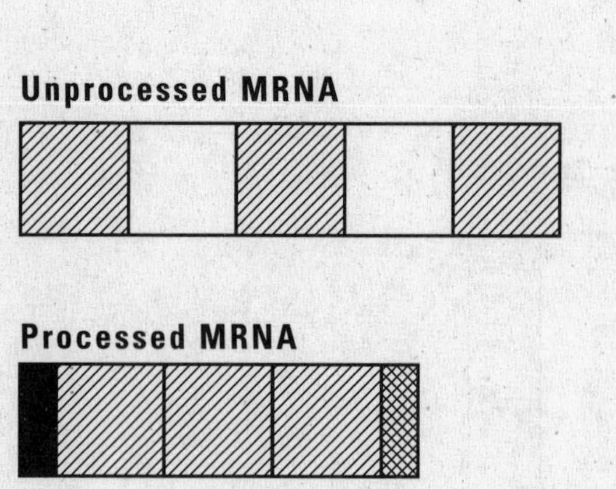

Legend

 ______________________

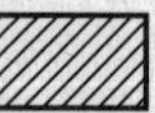 ______________________

 ______________________

 ______________________

Vocabulary Check

14. What is the difference between an exon and an intron?

____

____

15. Make an analogy to help you remember what a promoter is.

____

Name Period Date

SECTION 8.6

GENE EXPRESSION AND REGULATION

Power Notes

Promoter:

Operon:

lac operon:

Without lactose:

With lactose:

Controlling transcription in eukaryotic cells:

mRNA processing:

-
-
-

Name Period Date

SECTION **8.6** | GENE EXPRESSION AND REGULATION

Reinforcement

KEY CONCEPT Gene expression is carefully regulated in both prokaryotic and eukaryotic cells.

The regulation of gene expression better allows cells to respond to their environment and to interact in a coordinated manner. Controlling the start of transcription is important in both prokaryotic cells and eukaryotic cells. It is especially important in prokaryotic cells because there is no separation between DNA and the cytoplasm.

In prokaryotic cells, genes are often organized into **operons,** which are sets of genes that code for all of the proteins needed to carry out a particular task. These genes are transcribed as a unit, and they are often controlled by a DNA sequence called a promoter. **Promoters** help RNA polymerase know where a gene starts. One of the first operons to be discovered was the *lac* operon, which is involved in the breakdown of the sugar lactose. The *lac* promoter acts like a switch. When lactose is absent, a repressor protein binds to the promoter and blocks RNA polymerase from transcribing the *lac* genes. When lactose is present, it binds to the repressor protein. This action blocks the repressor from binding to the promoter. As a result, RNA polymerase can transcribe the *lac* genes, and lactose is broken down.

The start of transcription is still a very important point of regulation in eukaryotic cells as well. Eukaryotes also have DNA sequences that help regulate transcription. These include promoters, enhancers, and silencers. Some sequences are found in almost all eukaryotic cells, such as the TATA box. Others are more specific. Each gene has a unique combination of sequences and transcription factors, proteins that recognize DNA sequences and help RNA polymerase recognize the start of a gene. Regulating the expression of genes that control the expression of other genes is critical to the normal development of an organism.

The mRNA in eukaryotic cells undergoes processing. An mRNA strand is a patchwork of sequences that are either expressed in the protein or are cut out. The expressed sequences are called **exons;** the sequences removed during processing are called **introns.** In addition, a cap is added that helps prevent break down and directs the mRNA to a ribosome. A tail is added that helps the mRNA strand exit the nucleus.

1. How does the presence of lactose enable RNA polymerase to transcribe the *lac* genes?

____

____

2. What types of DNA sequences help eukaryotic cells regulate gene expression?

____

3. What happens during mRNA processing?

____

Name Period Date

SECTION 8.7 | MUTATIONS
Study Guide

KEY CONCEPT

Mutations are changes in DNA that may or may not affect phenotype.

VOCABULARY	
mutation	frameshift mutation
point mutation	mutagen

MAIN IDEA: Some mutations affect a single gene, while others affect an entire chromosome.

1. List two types of gene mutations.

____

2. List two types of chromosomal mutations.

____

3. Which type of mutation affects more genes, a gene mutation or a chromosomal mutation?

____

4. What leads to gene duplication?

____

5. What is a translocation?

____

Below is a string of nucleotides. **(1)** Use brackets to indicate the reading frame of the nucleotide sequence. **(2)** Copy the nucleotide sequence into the first box and make a point mutation. Circle the mutation. **(3)** Copy the nucleotide sequence into the second box and make a frameshift mutation. Use brackets to indicate how the reading frame would be altered by the mutation.

A G G C G T C C A T G A
6.
7.

CHAPTER 8 From DNA to Proteins

Name Period Date

MAIN IDEA: Mutations may or may not affect phenotype.
Fill in the cause-and-effect diagram below to explain how a point mutation may or may not affect phenotype.

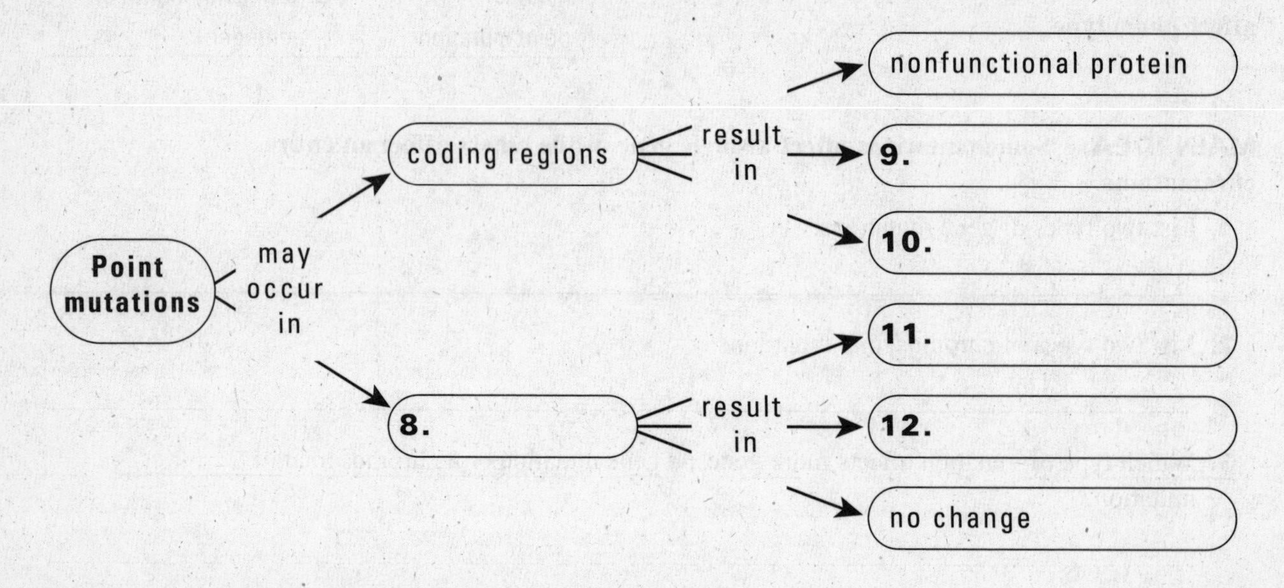

13. For a mutation to be passed to offspring, in what type of cell must it occur?

____

MAIN IDEA: Mutations can be caused by several factors.

14. Can DNA polymerase catch and correct every replication error?

____

15. What is a mutagen?

____

16. How does UV light damage the DNA strand?

____

____

Vocabulary Check

17. What is a mutation?

____

18. If a nucleotide is deleted from a strand of DNA, what type of mutation has occurred?

____

Name Period Date

SECTION **8.7** | MUTATIONS
Power Notes

Gene Mutations:

-
-

Chromosomal Mutations:

-
-

Mutations

Potential impact:

Silent:

Mutagens:

Name Period Date

SECTION 8.7 | MUTATIONS

Reinforcement

KEY CONCEPT Mutations are changes in DNA that may or may not affect phenotype.

A **mutation** is a change in an organism's DNA. Although a cell has mechanisms to deal with mutations, exposure to mutagens may cause mutations to happen more quickly than the body can repair them. **Mutagens** are agents in the environment that can change DNA. Some occur naturally, such as UV light from the Sun. Many other mutagens are industrial chemicals.

Mutations may affect individual genes or an entire chromosome. Gene mutations include point mutations and frameshift mutations.

- A **point mutation** is a substitution in a single nucleotide.
- A **frameshift mutation** involves the insertion or deletion of a nucleotide or nucleotides. It throws off the reading frame of the codons that come after the mutation.

Chromosomal mutations include gene duplications and translocations. Gene duplication is the result of improper alignment during crossing over. It results in one chromosome having two copies of certain genes, and the other chromosome having no copies of those genes. Translocation is the movement of a piece of one chromosome to another, nonhomologous chromosome.

Mutations may or may not affect phenotype. Chromosomal mutations affect many genes and tend to have a large effect on an organism. They may also cause breaks in the middle of a gene, causing that gene to no longer function or to make a hybrid with a new function. The effect of a gene mutation can also vary widely. For example, a point mutation may occur in the third nucleotide of a codon and have no effect on the amino acid coded for. Or the mutation may occur in an intron and thus have no effect. However, the mutation might result in the incorporation of an incorrect amino acid that messes up protein folding and function. Or it might code for a premature stop codon. Even mutations that occur in noncoding regions of DNA can have significant effects if they disrupt a splice site or a DNA sequence involved in gene regulation. For a mutation to affect offspring, it must occur in an organism's germ cells.

1. What is a mutation?

____

2. In a frameshift mutation, what is the "frame" that is being shifted?

____

3. How might a point mutation in a gene affect the resulting protein?

____

____

Name Period Date

CHAPTER 8 | INTERPRETING HISTOGRAMS

Data Analysis Practice

A histogram is a type of bar graph used to show the frequency distribution of data. The independent variable is usually shown on the *x*-axis and the dependent variable is shown on the *y*-axis.

In the example below, a scientist determined the number of base pairs in different species including *E. coli,* baker's yeast, an RNA retrovirus, a lily plant, a fruit fly, a frog, and a shark. She decided to compile the data into categories based on the number of organisms that had a certain number of base pairs. The histogram shows the frequency distribution of the data.

GRAPH 1. NUMBER OF BASE PAIRS IN VARIOUS ORGANISMS

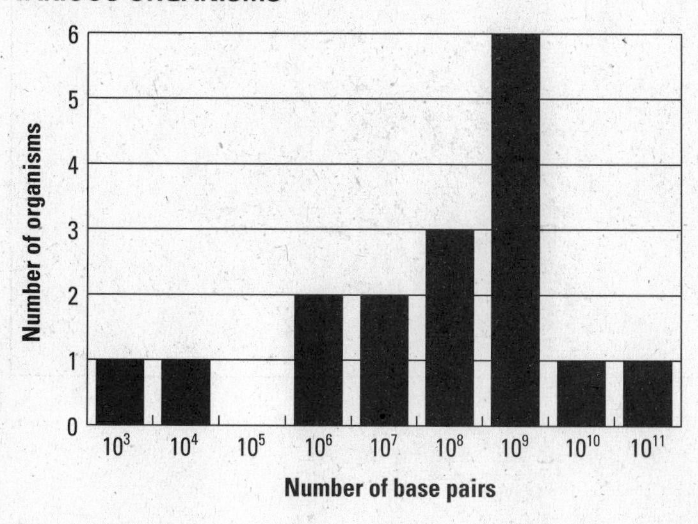

1. **Identify** How many species in the study had base pairs that numbered in the hundreds of millions?

____

____

2. **Synthesize** Suppose more data have been collected since the study above was completed. There are two more species with base pairs of 10^5 and one more species with base pairs of 10^{10}. Construct a graph that includes the new data.

Name Period Date

Name Period Date

CHAPTER 8 | MODELING DNA STRUCTURE

Pre-AP Activity

In Chapter 8, you have learned about the three-dimensional structure of DNA. In the early 1950s, several groups of researchers raced to be the first to determine the details of DNA structure. At the time, consensus was growing that the DNA molecule consisted of a fiber that was spiral shaped, and formed either a double or triple helix.

Scientists already knew DNA was a nucleic acid made up of nitrogen-containing bases, phosphates, and sugars. They just weren't sure which of these components made up the outer strands or "chains" of the helix and which components formed the bonds connecting one chain to another. You know that James Watson and Francis Crick won the race. Their paper was published in *Nature* on April 25, 1953. Several excerpts from their historic paper follow.

PAULING-COREY MODEL

Excerpt "A structure for nucleic acid has already been proposed by Pauling and Corey. . . . Their model consists of three intertwined chains, with the phosphates near the fibre axis, and the bases on the outside."

Your Interpretation On a separate piece of paper, draw a diagram showing how the different components of the Pauling-Corey model would match up between just two of the three strands (chains). Assume an equal number of phosphates and bases. Use lines to represent bonds, circles to represent phosphates, and squares to represent bases. Draw just enough to give a sense of what the internal structure might look like. For the purpose of this activity, do not worry about the placement of the sugars.

FRASER MODEL

Excerpt "Another three-chain structure has also been suggested by Fraser . . . . In his model the phosphates are on the outside and the bases on the inside, linked together by hydrogen bonds."

Your Interpretation On a separate piece of paper, draw a diagram showing how the different components of the Fraser model would match up. This time use dotted or dashed lines for hydrogen bonds, otherwise use the same style you used for the Pauling-Corey Model.

WATSON-CRICK MODEL

The Watson and Crick model took shape after seeing Rosalind Franklin's x-ray image of DNA and having its details interpreted for them.

Excerpt "We wish to put forward a radically different structure for the salt of deoxyribonucleic acid. This structure has two helical chains each coiled round the same axis . . . the bases are on the inside of the helix and the phosphates on the outside. . . . The novel feature of the structure is the manner in which the two chains are held together by the purine and pyrmidine bases . . . One of the pair must be a purine and the other a pyrimidine for bonding to occur. . . . In other words, if an adenine forms one member of a pair, on either chain, then on these assumptions the other member must be thymine; similarly for guanine and cytosine.

Your Interpretation As before use a diagram to show how the different components of the Watson-Crick model match up. Use a dotted or dashed line for the hydrogen bonds that form between the bases. This time include the detail of the base pairs.

Name Period Date

ROSALIND FRANKLIN'S CONTRIBUTION

Rosalind Franklin's x-ray image of DNA and her explanation of it appeared in the same issue of *Nature* on April 25, 1953. An excerpt is given below. What she had contributed were the physical dimensions: DNA's density and size, and its water content. She determined that each turn of the helix is 34 angstroms long and contains 10 base pairs that are 3.4 angstroms apart and pitched at a certain angle. She calculated the diameter of the helix. Also critical to the Watson-Crick model was her conviction that, given all the physical evidence, the phosphates had to be on the outside.

Excerpt "Thus, if the structure is helical, we find that the phosphate groups . . . lie on a helix of diameter about 20 A., and the sugar and base groups must accordingly be turned inwards towards the helical axis."

Interestingly enough, Watson and Crick had been thinking along the same lines as Pauling and Corey, that the bases were on the outside, exposed and available to pass along genetic information. What Franklin understood, as a chemist, was that the hydrophilic ("water-loving") sugar-phosphates would be on the outside of the molecule and the hydrophobic ("water-fearing") base pairs on the inside.

1. Why does it make more sense for the hydrophilic sugar-phosphates to be on the outside of the DNA molecule and the hydrophobic nitrogenous bases on the inside? What other cellular structure do you know of that has a similar orientation?

____

____

____

____

____

Name Period Date

CHAPTER 8

INBORN ERRORS OF METABOLISM

Pre-AP Activity

In Chapter 2, you learned about the structure of proteins and enzymes. You learned in Chapter 6 that an allele is an alternative form of a gene and in Chapter 7 that some genes have multiple alleles. In Chapter 8 you have learned about the base sequences of DNA and how they can be altered by mutation. Now you will combine all this information to form a biochemical picture of inheritance.

ENZYMES

An enzyme is functional only when its three-dimensional structure is intact. This structure is necessary for normal function because the substrate must fit precisely into the enzyme's active site to catalyze a reaction. Any change in an amino acid located at a critical position in the active site can make the enzyme nonfunctional.

Most metabolic processes involve a pathway of several chemical reactions, rather than a single reaction, meaning several enzymes are needed to produce the final product. Compound A may be broken down to form compound B, which forms compound C, and so on. If any one of the enzymes in the pathway becomes nonfunctional, that step is blocked and no final product can be made. In addition, the reactant in the blocked reaction accumulates in the body. Many of these intermediate compounds are toxic.

MUTATIONS

When a base in DNA undergoes a point mutation, a codon in mRNA usually changes. When a codon changes, an amino acid in a protein may change, and when the amino acid sequence of an enzyme changes, its three-dimensional structure may change. Whether the structure changes or not depends on where in the protein the altered amino acid is located and how similar the properties of the new amino acid are to those of the original amino acid. An amino acid change in a non-critical part of the enzyme may have no effect. However, the substitution of a polar amino acid for a nonpolar amino acid, or an acidic amino acid for a basic amino acid, can completely disrupt the structure of the enzyme.

ALLELES

Whenever there is a mutation that causes a change in a metabolic pathway, a new allele can result. Theoretically, any base in a gene can mutate. Why, then, doesn't each gene have hundreds or thousands of alleles? Because only a very small minority of the bases in a gene actually code for amino acid sequence of the enzyme. For example, in one particular gene with about 90,000 bases, only 1,356 bases code for amino acids. Much of the remainder is involved in regulation or has no known function.

Most mutations result in a nonfunctional enzyme. A gene has only two alleles—one for a functioning enzyme and one for a nonfunctioning enzyme. Some genes have multiple alleles, although any individual can have only two. These alleles usually reflect amino acid changes in an enzyme that reduce the enzyme's effectiveness but do not completely destroy its functionality.

Name Period Date

Metabolic pathway for the breakdown of phenylalanine

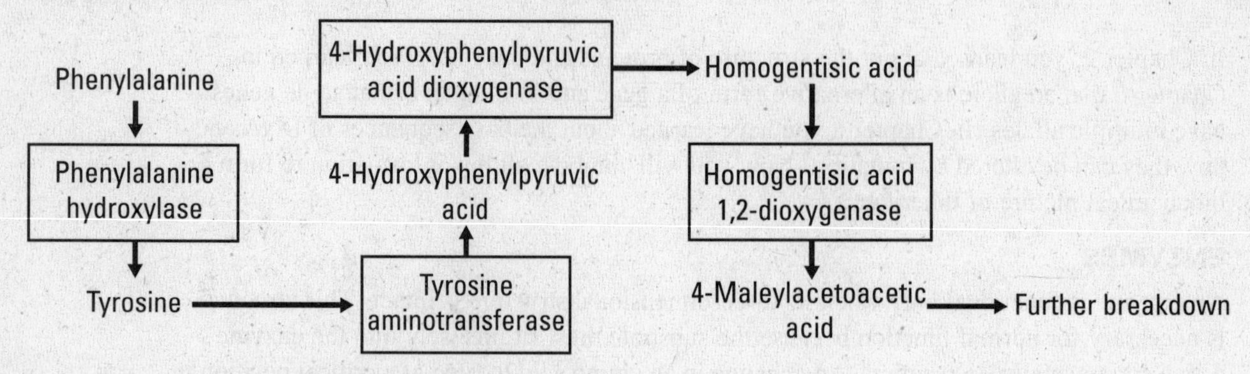

ANALYSIS OF A BIOCHEMICAL PATHWAY

In 1909, the British physician Archibald Garrod coined the term *inborn error of metabolism* to describe an inherited disease called alkaptonuria. Alkaptonuria is a rare disease in which a person excretes homogentisic acid in his or her urine.

Homogentisic acid is formed from the breakdown of amino acids phenylalanine and tyrosine, which are found in most protein foods. When the enzyme that breaks down homogentisic acid is defective, the biochemical pathway is blocked. Homogentisic acid accumulates in the body until it is removed in the urine.

Examine the biochemical pathway shown below. Each step in the pathway requires a different enzyme, and each enzyme is coded by a different gene. Including alkaptonuria, there are genetic diseases caused by defective enzymes in each of the steps of this metabolic pathway.

- phenylketonuria (PKU)—phenylalanine hydroxylase is defective
- tyrosinemia type II—tyrosine aminotransferase is defective
- tyrosinemia type III—4-hydroxyphenylpyruvic acid dioxygenase is defective

These three diseases result in mental retardation and other serious health problems.

1. What compound accumulates in the blood of people who have PKU? ____________________

2. What compound accumulates in people who have tyrosinemia type II? ____________________

3. What compound accumulates in people who have tyrosinemia type III? ____________________

4. Which enzyme is defective in people with alkaptonuria? ____________________

5. Babies born in the United States are routinely tested for PKU after birth. How might the symptoms of this disease be prevented in a baby who tests positive for PKU? ____________________

____

6. Would a baby with PKU be damaged by being fed tyrosine? Explain. ____________________

____

CHAPTER 8
From DNA to Proteins

Name Period Date

CHAPTER 8 | FROM DNA TO PROTEINS

Vocabulary Practice

bacteriophage	RNA polymerase	promoter
nucleotide	messenger RNA (mRNA)	operon
double helix	ribosomal RNA (rRNA)	exon
base pairing rules	transfer RNA (tRNA)	intron
replication	translation	mutation
DNA polymerase	codon	point mutation
central dogma	stop codon	frameshift mutation
RNA	start codon	mutagen
transcription	anticodon	

A. Compound Word Puzzle Read the phrase and write the word that it most closely describes. Then write another phrase that describes the same word in a different way.

PHRASE 1	WORD	PHRASE 2
error that throws off the reading frame of an mRNA sequence	**Example** *frameshift mutation*	*caused by insertion or deletion of nucleotides*
explains Chargaff's rules	**1.**	
states that genetic information flows in one direction	**2.**	
pairs with an mRNA codon during translation	**3.**	
an intervening sequence	**4.**	
the type of RNA that is converted to a protein during translation	**5.**	

Name Period Date

VOCABULARY PRACTICE, CONTINUED

PHRASE 1	WORD	PHRASE 2
a change in an organism's DNA	6.	
monomer that makes up nucleic acids	7.	
a sequence of mRNA that is expressed after processing	8.	

B. Find the Odd Word Put a checkmark next to the word that does not belong.

1. ____ mutagen
   ____ rRNA
   ____ tRNA

   Explanation________________________________

2. ____ codon
   ____ mRNA
   ____ replication

   Explanation________________________________

3. ____ central dogma
   ____ mutagen
   ____ mutation

   Explanation________________________________

4. ____ codon
   ____ double helix
   ____ frameshift mutation

   Explanation________________________________

4. ____ bacteriophage
   ____ RNA polymerase
   ____ transcription

   Explanation________________________________

CHAPTER 8
From DNA to Proteins

C. Secret Message Next to each definition, fill in the blanks with the vocabulary word that best fits each description. When complete, write the boxed letters in order in the blanks at the bottom of the page to answer the clue.

1. large enzyme that initiates transcription ____ ____ ____ ____ [ ] ____ ____ ____ ____ ____ ____ ____ ____ ____ ____ ____ ____

2. caused by the insertion or deletion of nucleotides in DNA ____ [ ] ____ ____ ____ ____ ____ ____ ____ ____ ____ ____ ____ ____ ____ ____ ____ ____ ____

3. spliced together during mRNA processing ____ ____ [ ] ____

4. part of a ribosome; catalyzes the formation of peptide bonds between amino acids ____ ____ ____ ____ ____ ____ ____ ____ [ ] ____ ____ ____ ____ ____

5. a change in a single nucleotide in DNA ____ [ ] ____ ____ ____ ____ ____ ____ ____ ____ ____ ____ ____ ____ ____

6. examples include radiation and UV light ____ ____ [ ] ____ ____ ____ ____

7. made up of a sugar, a phosphate group, and a nitrogen-containing base ____ ____ ____ ____ ____ ____ ____ ____ ____ [ ]

8. the part of the central dogma that occurs in the cytoplasm of eukaryotic cells ____ [ ] ____ ____ ____ ____ ____ ____ ____ ____ ____

9. Fill in the blanks with the boxed letters from above to name a region of DNA where RNA polymerase binds: ____ ____ ____ ____ ____ ____ ____ ____

Name Period Date

D. DNA Adventure! Solve the clues by filling in the words in the numbered squares.

Across

2. the process that makes a polypeptide
4. A, C, G, and T in DNA; A, C, G, and U in RNA
5. component of ribosomes
12. process that involves RNA polymerase
15. sequence in mRNA that is not expressed as protein
16. three-dimensional model developed by Watson and Crick
17. the rules that explain how nucleotides interact with each other

Down

1. a change in a single nucleotide in DNA
3. the process of making a copy of DNA
6. complementary to an mRNA codon
7. carries an amino acid from the cytoplasm to a ribosome
8. major enzyme involved in replication
9. describes the flow of genetic information
10. used by Hershey and Chase in their experiments
11. may be induced by mutagens
13. halts translation
14. helps RNA polymerase recognize the start of a gene

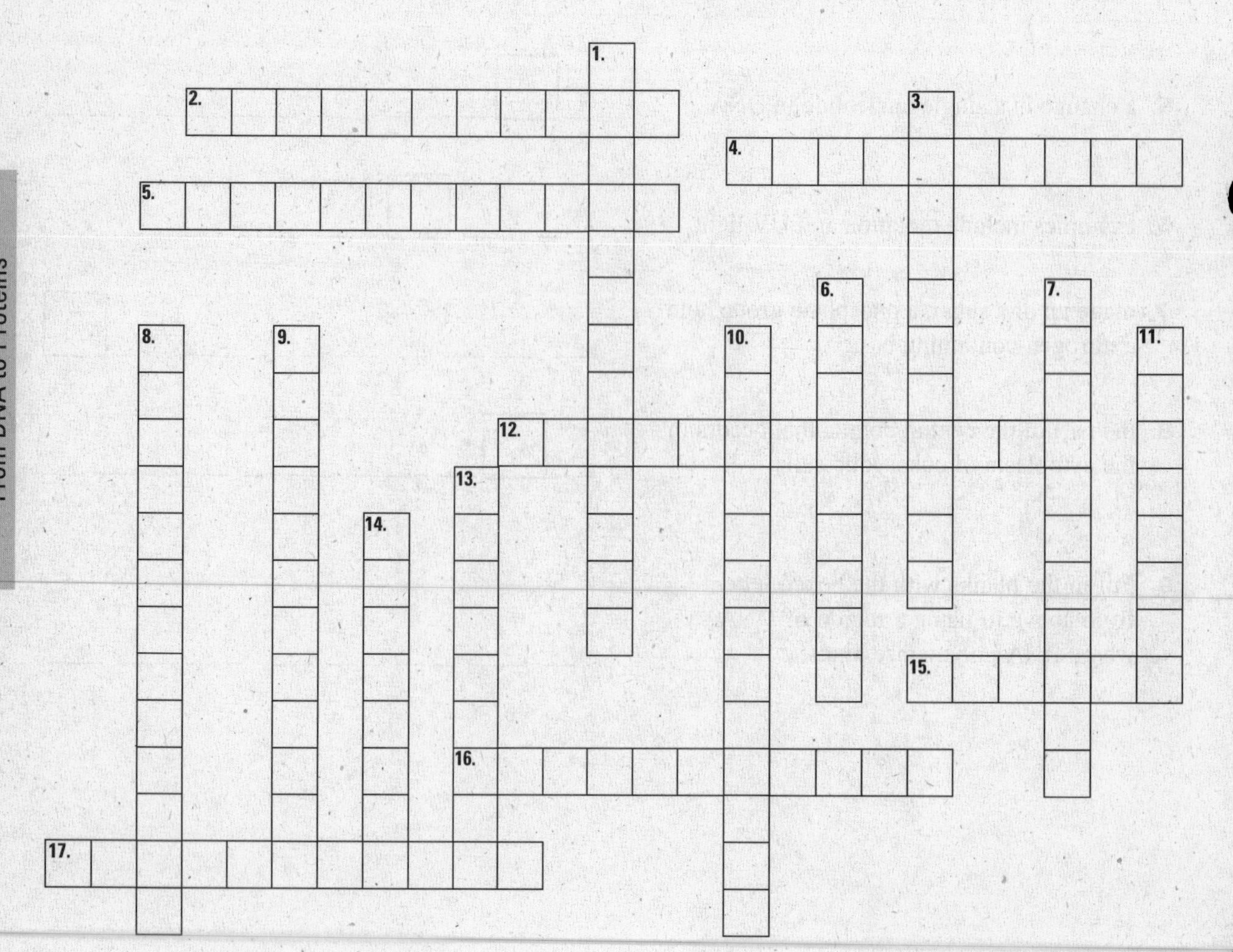

Name Period Date

SECTION **9.1** | MANIPULATING DNA

Study Guide

KEY CONCEPT
Biotechnology relies on cutting DNA at specific places.

VOCABULARY	
restriction enzyme	restriction map
gel electrophoresis	

MAIN IDEA: Scientists use several techniques to manipulate DNA.

1. List five ways in which scientists study and manipulate DNA.

____

____

MAIN IDEA: Restriction enzymes cut DNA.

2. What is a restriction enzyme?

____

3. What is the nucleotide sequence at which a restriction enzyme cuts DNA called?

____

4. Why would different restriction enzymes cut the same DNA molecule into different numbers of fragments?

____

In the space provided below, draw two sketches. Show what happens when a restriction enzyme leaves "blunt ends," and show what happens when a restriction enzyme leaves "sticky ends." Label the restriction sites in each sketch.

Blunt Ends	Sticky Ends

MAIN IDEA: Restriction maps show the lengths of DNA fragments.

5. After DNA is cut with a restriction enzyme, how is the mixture of DNA fragments sorted?

6. How does gel electrophoresis work?

7. How do different fragments of DNA show up on a gel?

8. What information does a restriction map give about DNA? What information is not given by a restriction map?

9. How are restriction maps used?

Vocabulary Check

10. How does a restriction enzyme limit, or restrict, the effect of a virus on a bacterial cell?

11. The prefix *electro-* means "electricity." The suffix *-phoresis* comes from a Greek word that means "carrying." How do these two meanings relate to what happens in gel electrophoresis?

Name Period Date

SECTION 9.1 | MANIPULATING DNA

Power Notes

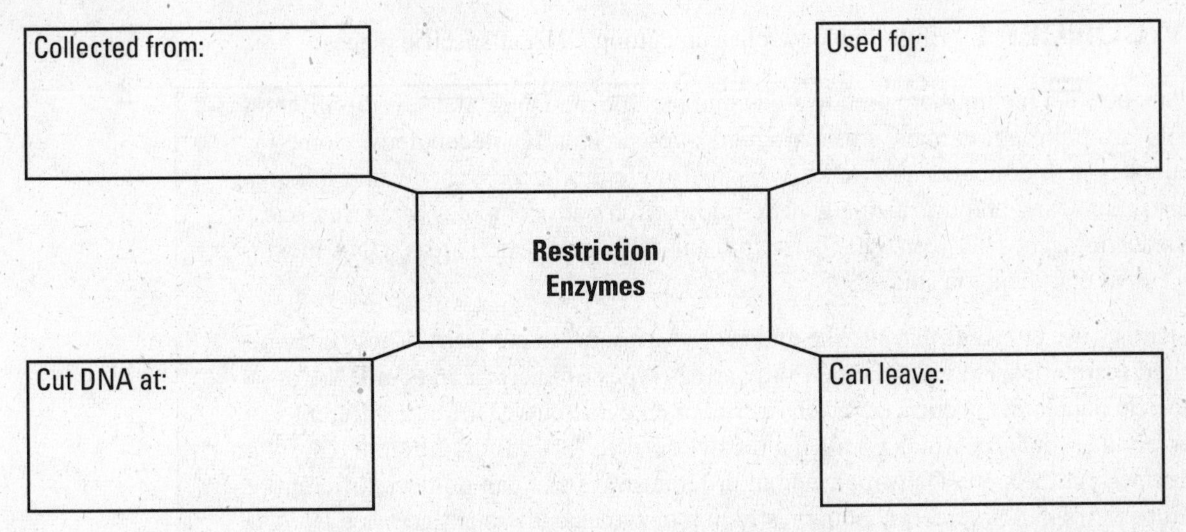

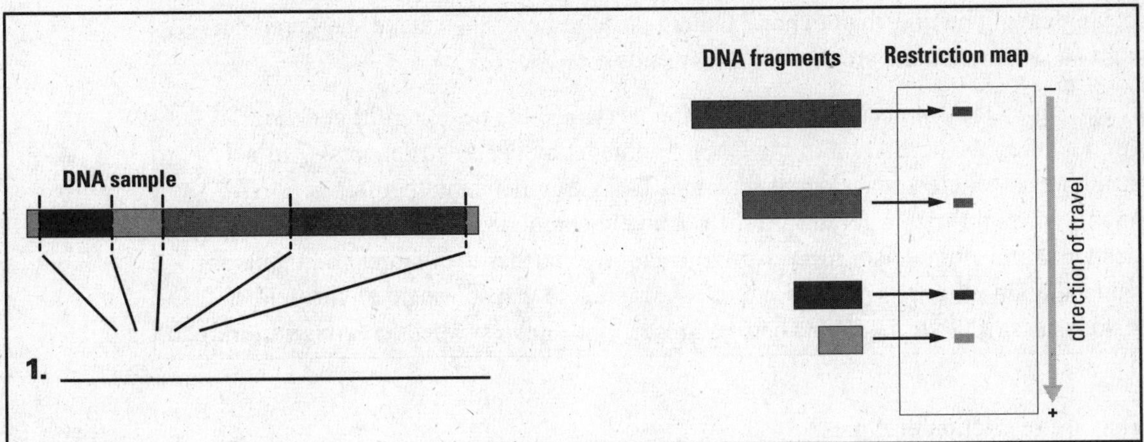

1. ______________________________

Gel electrophoresis:

•

•

Restriction maps show:

•

•

Name Period Date

SECTION **9.1** | MANIPULATING DNA

Reinforcement

KEY CONCEPT Biotechnology relies on cutting DNA at specific places.

Many indirect methods are used to study and manipulate DNA, and several different tools are important in many areas of genetics research and biotechnology. Some examples include sequencing genes, copying (or cloning) genes, chemically mutating genes, analyzing and organizing genetic information with computer databases, and transferring genes between organisms. In many of these research areas, DNA must first be cut so that it can be studied.

Scientists use enzymes that act like molecular "scissors" to cut DNA. These enzymes, called **restriction enzymes,** come from various types of bacteria and cut DNA at specific nucleotide sequences. Each restriction enzyme cuts DNA at a different nucleotide sequence, which is called a restriction site. As a result, different restriction enzymes cut the same DNA molecule in different ways and can produce different numbers of DNA fragments. Some restriction enzymes cut straight across a DNA molecule, leaving behind "blunt ends." Other restriction enzymes make staggered cuts through a DNA molecule, producing "sticky ends."

After cutting a DNA molecule with restriction enzymes, the next step in genetics research is often the separation of the DNA fragments by gel electrophoresis. In gel electrophoresis, an electrical current separates DNA fragments by their sizes. DNA fragments travel through a gel toward the positively charged pole, but pores in the gel slow down larger fragments. Smaller fragments travel farther than larger fragments in the same amount of time. The pattern of DNA fragments that shows up on the gel, which shows the sizes of DNA fragments between restriction sites, is called a **restriction map.**

1. What are restriction enzymes?

____

____

2. How does gel electrophoresis work?

____

____

____

3. What does a restriction map show?

____

____

Name Period Date

SECTION **9.2** | COPYING DNA

Study Guide

KEY CONCEPT

The polymerase chain reaction rapidly copies segments of DNA.

VOCABULARY
polymerase chain reaction (PCR)
primer

MAIN IDEA: PCR uses polymerases to copy DNA segments.

1. What is PCR?

____

2. Why is PCR useful?

____

MAIN IDEA: PCR is a three-step process.

3. What four materials are needed for PCR?

____

4. Why are primers needed in the PCR process?

____

Sketch and label the PCR process in the cycle below.

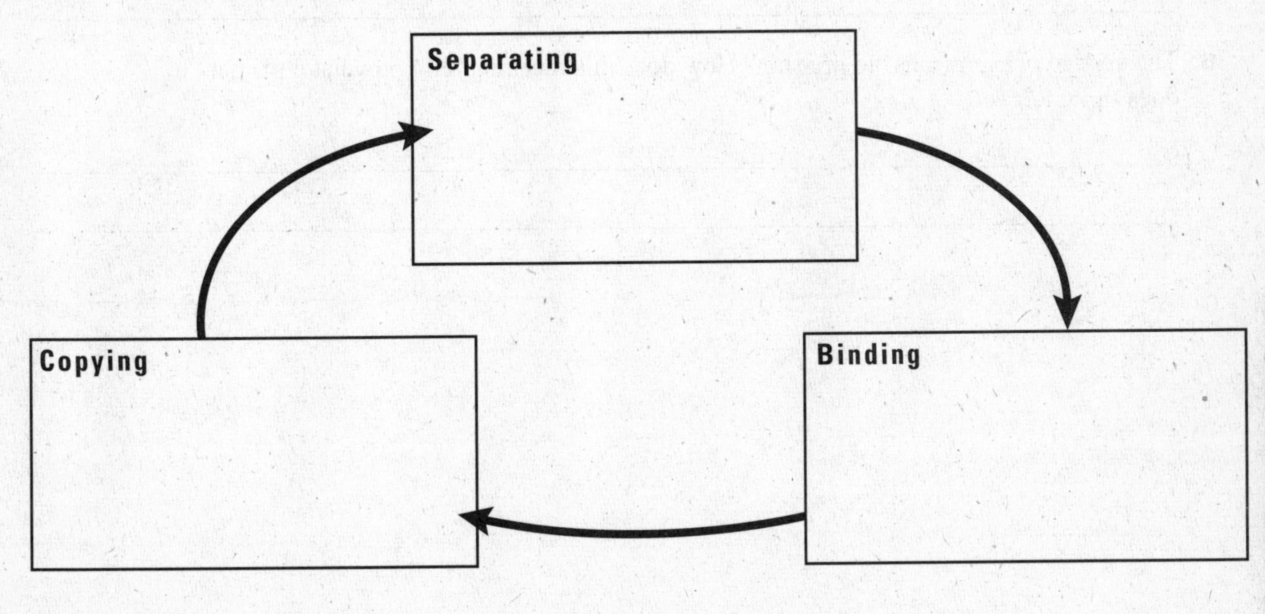

Sketch how the amount of DNA changes during five PCR cycles.

Vocabulary Check

5. DNA polymerase is an enzyme that helps put DNA molecules together. A chain reaction is a process in which one event leads to the next event and the effect is stronger over time. How does the combination of these two terms describe what happens during PCR?

____

____

6. The verb *to prime* means "to prepare." How does this meaning tell you what a primer does in PCR?

____

____

Name Period Date

SECTION
9.2
COPYING DNA
Power Notes

Polymerase chain reaction is:

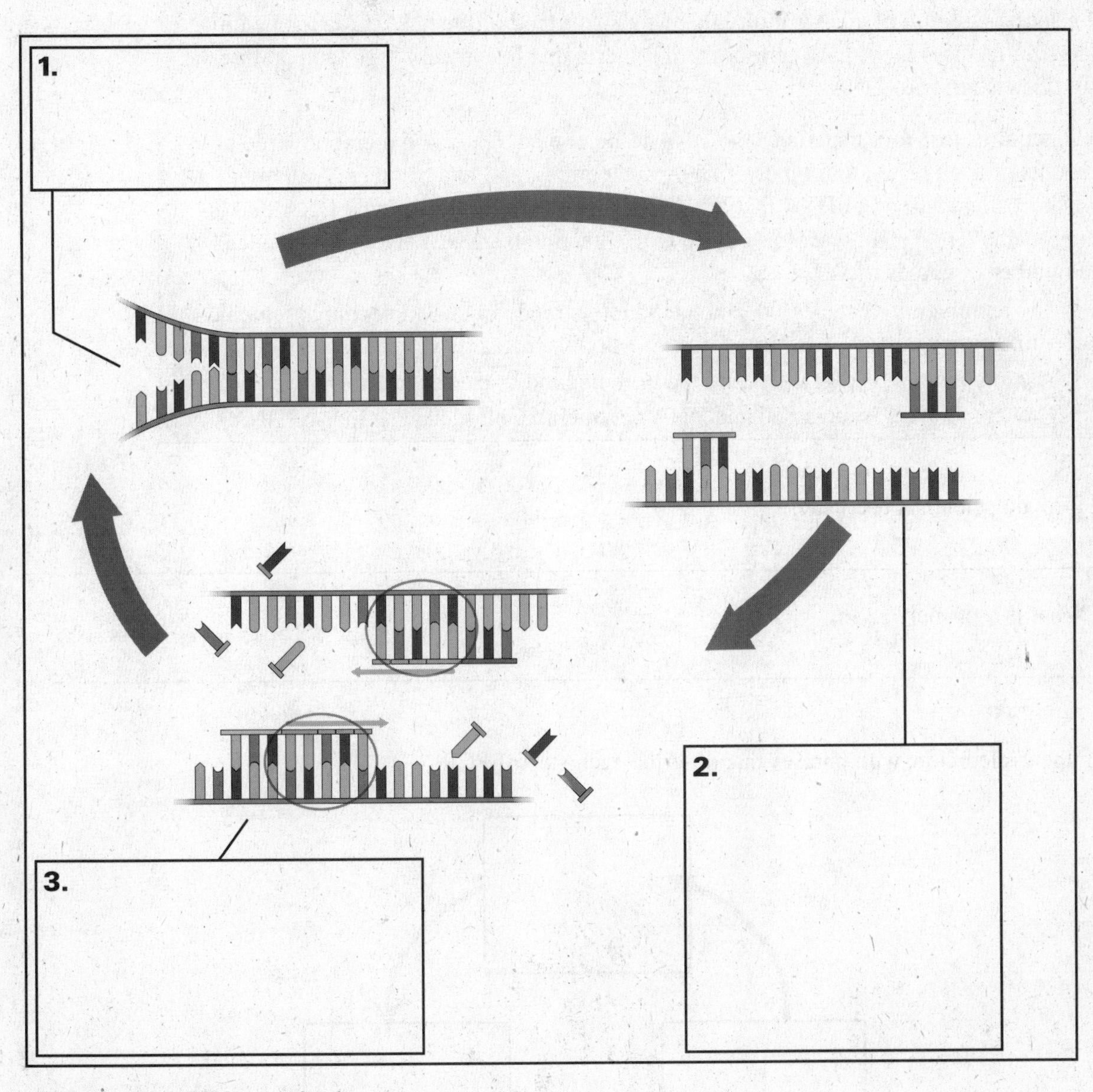

PCR amplifies DNA samples by:

Name Period Date

SECTION **9.2** | COPYING DNA
Reinforcement

KEY CONCEPT The polymerase chain reaction rapidly copies segments of DNA.

For many biotechnology applications, a sample of DNA is far too small to work with. A specific DNA sequence must be copied, or amplified, to produce a sample that is large enough to study. The **polymerase chain reaction (PCR)** makes a large number of copies of a specific region of a DNA molecule in a short period of time. PCR, developed by Kary Mullis, uses DNA polymerases from bacteria that live at very high temperatures to build new strands of DNA.

PCR requires just four materials: the DNA to be copied, DNA polymerases, large amounts of each of the four types of DNA nucleotides, and two primers. A **primer** is a short single strand of DNA that acts as the starting point for the new DNA that is being made. The PCR process is a cycle with three main steps. Each cycle doubles the number of copies of DNA.

- The temperature is increased, and the double-stranded DNA molecule is separated into single strands.
- The temperature is decreased, and the primers bind to the separated DNA strands.
- The temperature is increased and DNA polymerases build new strands of DNA.

1. Why do scientists use PCR?

____

2. What is a primer?

____

Fill in the cycle below with phrases that describe each step of PCR.

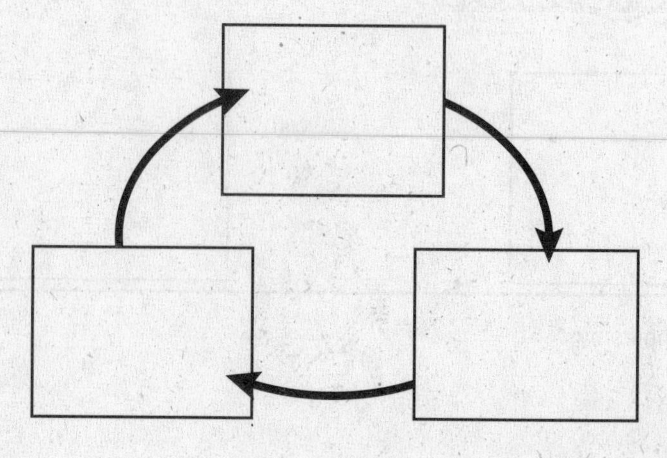

CHAPTER 9
Frontiers of Biotechnology

Name Period Date

SECTION 9.3 | DNA FINGERPRINTING

Study Guide

KEY CONCEPT

DNA fingerprints identify people at the molecular level.

VOCABULARY
DNA fingerprint

MAIN IDEA: A DNA fingerprint is a type of restriction map.

Take notes on DNA fingerprinting by filling in the main idea web below.

DNA fingerprint

1. Definition

2. What it shows

3. How it's made

4. What it's based on

5. How is a DNA fingerprint a specific type of restriction map?

____

____

MAIN IDEA: DNA fingerprinting is used for identification.

6. How does identification through DNA fingerprinting depend on probability?

7. The chance that two people have four repeats in location A is 1 in 100. The chance that two people have eight repeats in location B is 1 in 50. The probability that two people have three repeats in location C is 1 in 200. What is the probability that two people would have matching DNA fingerprints for these three locations by chance?

8. Why does using more regions of the genome decrease the probability that two people would have the same DNA fingerprint?

9. List two ways in which DNA fingerprinting is used for identification.

Vocabulary Check

10. One definition of the term *fingerprint* is "a distinctive mark or characteristic." How does this meaning relate to a DNA fingerprint?

Name Period Date

SECTION 9.3 | DNA FINGERPRINTING

Power Notes

DNA Fingerprinting

Based on:

-
-
-
-

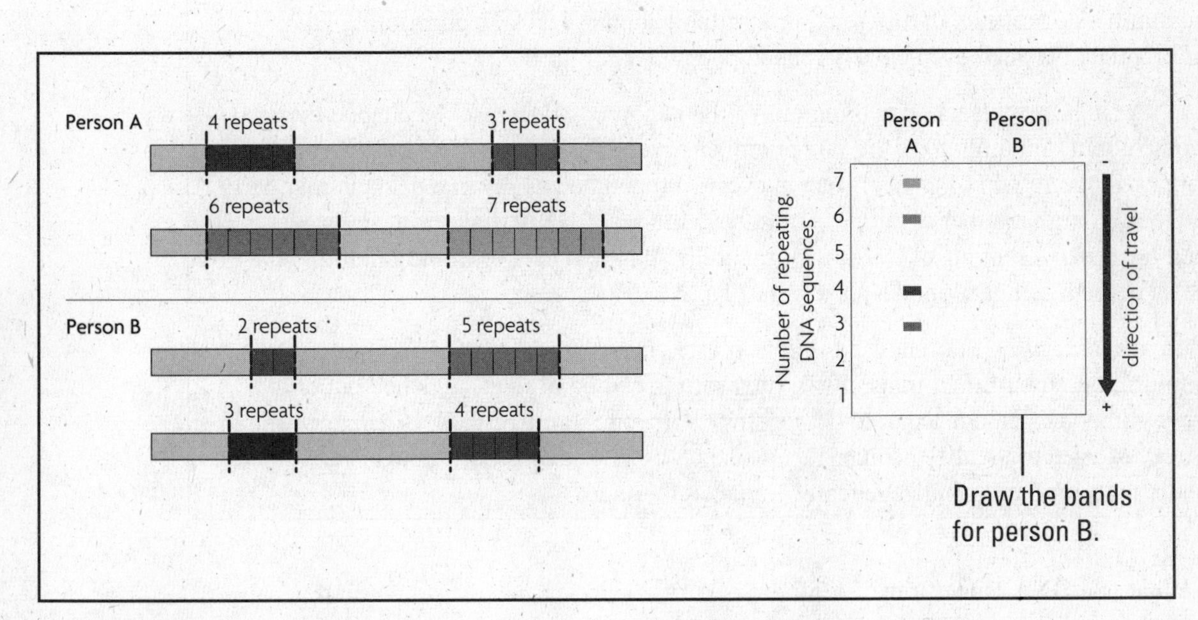

DNA fingerprinting and probability:

Uses of DNA fingerprinting:

Name Period Date

SECTION 9.3 | DNA FINGERPRINTING

Reinforcement

KEY CONCEPT DNA fingerprints identify people at the molecular level.

Everyone, with the exception of identical twins, has a unique set of DNA. This variation in DNA can be used to identify people through a process called DNA fingerprinting. A **DNA fingerprint** is a type of restriction map that can be used to identify people at the molecular level.

The greatest differences in DNA among people are found in the areas of DNA that do not code for proteins, or noncoding regions. For this reason, DNA fingerprinting is used to identify the differences in noncoding regions of DNA. In these noncoding regions, specific DNA sequences can be repeated over and over. Each person has a unique combination of the numbers of repeated sequences, or repeats. By finding the numbers of repeats in different parts of the genome, DNA fingerprinting can differentiate between even closely related people.

A DNA fingerprint tests several regions of the genome to decrease the chance that two people could randomly have the same number of repeats. Suppose DNA fingerprinting only used one region of DNA. If one in every 500 people has seven repeats in that part of DNA, a large number of people would have the same DNA fingerprint. However, by looking at many regions of DNA, the probability that two people would randomly have the same DNA fingerprint decreases sharply.

DNA fingerprinting is often used in legal cases, including criminal trials and immigration. In criminal trials, DNA fingerprints can be used as evidence either to prove someone's innocence or to demonstrate someone's guilt. But DNA fingerprinting is not just used to identify people. It can also be used to identify different species, study biodiversity, and to locate genetically engineered crops.

1. What is a DNA fingerprint?

____

2. What is a DNA fingerprint based on?

____

3. Why does a DNA fingerprint test several regions of DNA?

____

____

4. List three examples of how DNA fingerprinting is used.

____

____

Name Period Date

SECTION 9.4 | GENETIC ENGINEERING
Study Guide

KEY CONCEPT
DNA sequences of organisms can be changed.

VOCABULARY		
clone	recombinant DNA	transgenic
genetic engineering	plasmid	gene knockout

MAIN IDEA: Entire organisms can be cloned.
Fill in the chart below to take notes about cloning.

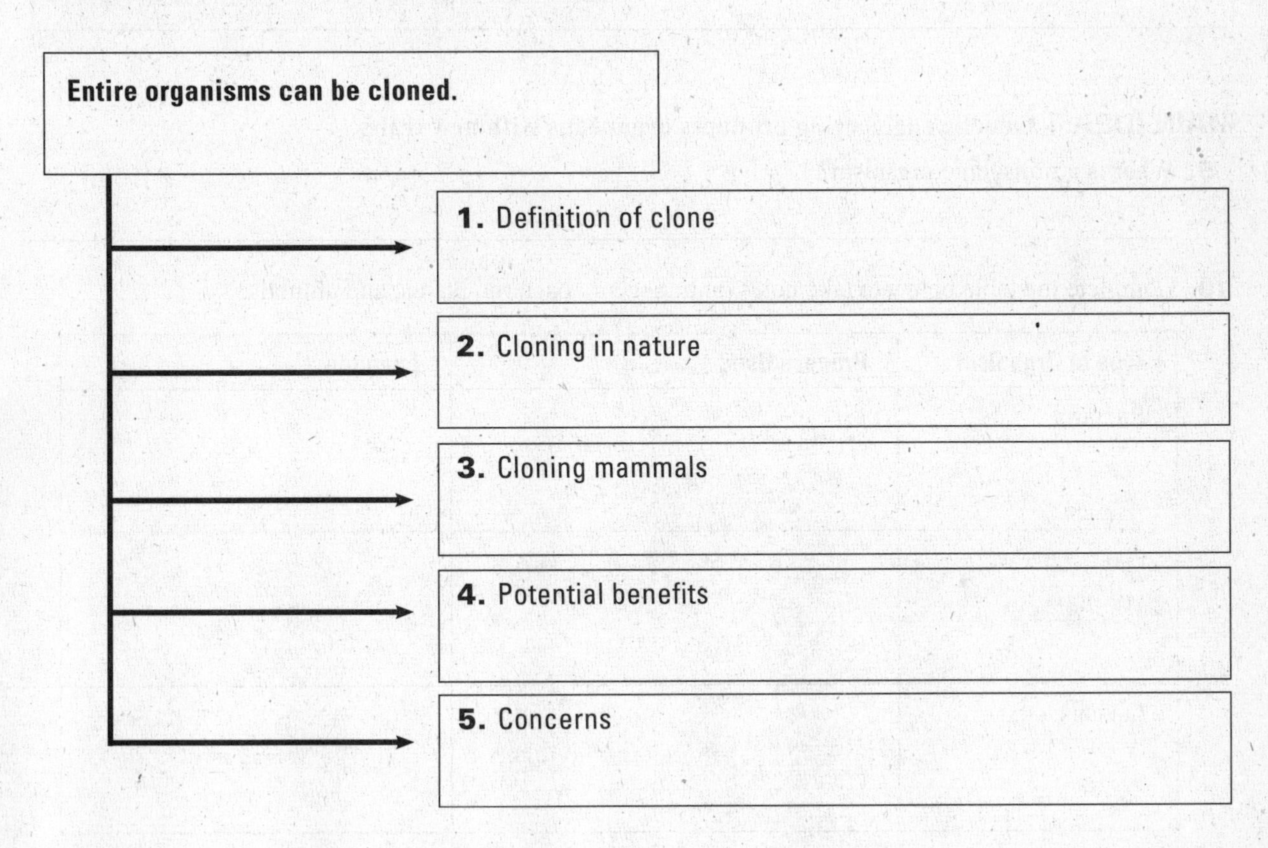

MAIN IDEA: New genes can be added to an organism's DNA.

6. What is genetic engineering?

____

7. What is recombinant DNA?

____

8. Why are plasmids used to produce bacteria with recombinant DNA?

____

CHAPTER 9
Frontiers of Biotechnology

Use the space below to sketch and label the process that scientists use to produce bacteria with recombinant DNA. Use Figure 9.11 help you with your sketch.

MAIN IDEA: Genetic engineering produces organisms with new traits.

9. What is a transgenic organism?

____

10. Complete the table below to take notes on transgenic bacteria, plants, and animals.

Type of Organism	Process Used	Example
Bacteria		
Plants		
Animals		

Vocabulary Check

11. The term *recombine* means "to combine, or join, again." How is the meaning of recombine related to the production of recombinant DNA?

____

12. The prefix *trans-* means "across," and *genic* means "relating to genes." How do these two meanings help to explain the meaning of *transgenic*?

____

Name Period Date

SECTION **9.4** GENETIC ENGINEERING

Power Notes

Cloning		
In nature:	Mammals:	Potential and controversy:

Genetic Engineering

Recombinant DNA:

Transgenic bacteria:	Transgenic plants:	Transgenic animals:

Concerns about genetic engineering:

Name Period Date

SECTION 9.4 | GENETIC ENGINEERING
Reinforcement

KEY CONCEPT DNA sequences of organisms can be changed.

Many of today's advances in biotechnology involve genetic engineering and cloning. A **clone** is a genetically identical copy of a gene or of an entire organism. Although cloning occurs in nature, and the cloning of plants has been done for hundreds of years, the ability to clone mammals is a recent development.

To clone a mammal, scientists use a process called nuclear transfer. The DNA from the organism to be cloned is inserted into an unfertilized egg cell that has had its nucleus removed. The success rate of cloning adult mammals is very low, and it may take several hundred attempts to produce just one clone.

Cloned, or copied, genes are inserted into the DNA of a different organism to give the organism a new trait. This changing an organism's DNA is called **genetic engineering.** Genetic engineering is based on the use of recombinant DNA. **Recombinant DNA** is DNA that contains genes from more than one organism. Bacteria with recombinant DNA are often used in biotechnology applications. To produce bacteria with recombinant DNA, a gene is inserted into a **plasmid,** which is a loop of DNA that is separate from the bacterial DNA. Bacteria with the recombinant plasmid make the gene's product. An organism that has a gene from a different organism is **transgenic.**

Although there is concern about potential long-term effects of some genetically engineered organisms, transgenic plants and animals have been produced and are used in several different ways. Many types of transgenic crop plants, also called genetically modified (GM) crop plants, have been engineered to resist insects, frost, and diseases. Transgenic mice are frequently used in medical research.

Term	Definition	Example or Use
Clone	1.	2.
Genetic engineering	3.	4.
Recombinant DNA	5.	6.
Plasmid	7.	8.
Transgenic	9.	10.

Name Period Date

SECTION 9.5 | GENOMICS AND BIOINFORMATICS
Study Guide

KEY CONCEPT
Entire genomes are sequenced, studied, and compared.

VOCABULARY		
genomics	Human Genome Project	DNA microarray
gene sequencing	bioinformatics	proteomics

MAIN IDEA: Genomics involves the study of genes, gene functions, and entire genomes.
Take notes on concepts in genomics by completing the concept map below.

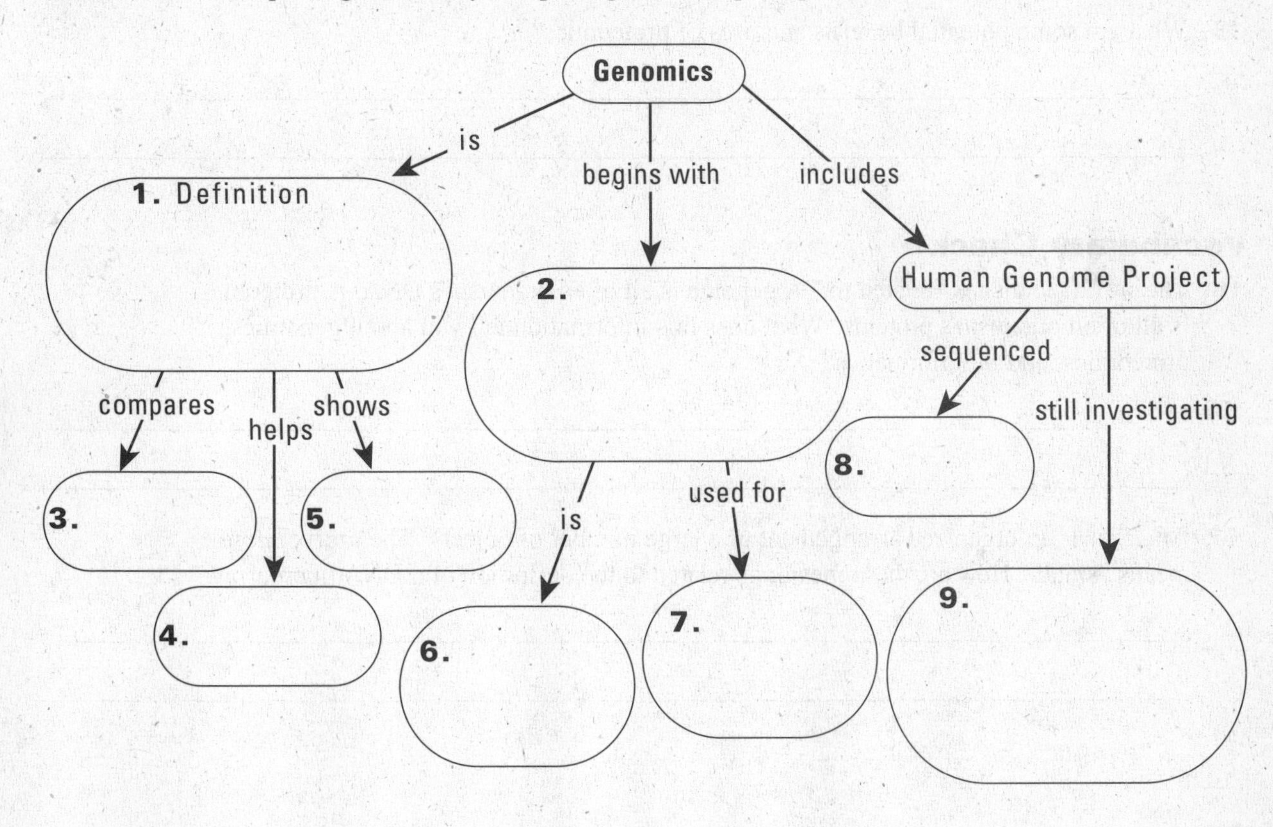

MAIN IDEA: Technology allows the study and comparison of both genes and proteins.

10. What is bioinformatics?

____

11. Why is bioinformatics important for genomics research?

____

12. What are DNA microarrays?

____

13. How can DNA microarrays compare gene expression in different cells?

14. What is proteomics?

15. What are some potential benefits and uses of proteomics?

Vocabulary Check

16. The suffix *-ic* means "related to." A genome is all of an organism's DNA. A proteome is all of an organism's proteins. What does this information tell you about genomics, proteomics, and bioinformatics?

17. An *array* is an organized arrangement or a large number of objects. The prefix *micro-* means "small." How are these meanings related to the definition of a DNA microarray.

Name Period Date

SECTION 9.5 | GENOMICS AND BIOINFORMATICS

Power Notes

Gene sequencing:

Genomics:

Human Genome Project:

Bioinformatics:	DNA microarrays:	Proteomics:

Name Period Date

SECTION **9.5** GENOMICS AND BIOINFORMATICS

Reinforcement

KEY CONCEPT Entire genomes are studied, sequenced, and compared.

An organism's genome is all of its genetic information. **Genomics** is the study of genomes, which includes the sequencing of all of an organism's DNA. By comparing genomes both within and among species, scientists can study evolutionary relationships, identify genes related to diseases, and learn about interactions among genes. All studies of genomics rely on **gene sequencing,** or finding the order of DNA nucleotides in genes or in whole genomes.

The complete genomes of more than 100 different types of organisms have been sequenced. Scientists use the genomes of other organisms—such as yeast, bacteria, fruit flies, plants, and mammals other than humans—to study genetics and for applications to humans. Only recently was the sequencing of the human genome completed. But, despite the great achievement of the **Human Genome Project** in sequencing the human genome, a great deal of work is still necessary to identify genes, find their locations, and determine their functions.

Genomes of different organisms differ greatly in size, from the 4.6 million nucleotide base pairs in *E. coli* bacteria, to the 139 billion base pairs in the lungfish. With all of the base pairs, genes, and proteins for which the genes code, large amounts of data are produced. **Bioinformatics** is the use of computer databases to organize and analyze biological data. Genomics has also led to advances in studying interactions among genes and in the proteins that result from the information in a genome.

- **DNA microarrays** are tiny chips that can be used to identify gene expression in different types of cells.
- **Proteomics** is the study and comparison of proteins within and among species.

1. What is genomics?

____

____

2. What did the Human Genome Project accomplish?

____

____

3. Why is bioinformatics useful in genomics?

____

____

Name Period Date

SECTION **9.6** | GENETIC SCREENING AND GENE THERAPY

Study Guide

KEY CONCEPT

Genetics provides a basis for new medical treatments.

VOCABULARY
genetic screening
gene therapy

MAIN IDEA: Genetic screening can detect genetic disorders.

1. What is the purpose of genetic screening?

____

2. How is genetic screening used?

____

MAIN IDEA: Gene therapy is the replacement of faulty genes.

3. What is the goal of gene therapy?

____

4. What are two technical challenges in gene therapy?

____

____

5. What is one experimental method for the treatment of cancer?

____

____

Vocabulary Check

6. The verb *to screen* means "to examine." Explain how this meaning is related to genetic screening.

____

7. What is gene therapy?

____

Advertise or Fight Against Genetic Screening

Choose one of the two following situations.

1. Suppose you work for a company that does genetic screening. Draw and write a one-page advertisement that explains genetic screening and what it both can and cannot do.

2. Suppose you are a spokesperson for a group that is against genetic screening. Draw and write a one-page advertisement that focuses on the ethical questions surrounding genetic screening.

Name Period Date

SECTION
9.6

GENETIC SCREENING AND GENE THERAPY

Power Notes

Genetic screening:

Detecting genetic disorders:

Detecting disease risk:

Gene therapy is:

Experimental Methods Used		
Genetically engineered viruses:	Stimulate immune system:	Insert "suicide gene":

Technical challenges include:

-
-
-

Name Period Date

SECTION **9.6** GENETIC SCREENING AND GENE THERAPY

Reinforcement

KEY CONCEPT Genetics provides a basis for new medical treatments.

The detection of alleles that may be involved in human diseases and genetic disorders can be done through the testing of a person's DNA. This process, called **genetic screening,** can help determine whether a person is at risk for developing or passing on a genetic disorder. Usually, genetic screening is used to search for specific genes that are known to be related to a particular illness. Genetic screening can detect genes that increase a person's risk of developing various types of cancer. It can also detect different inherited disorders, such as cystic fibrosis.

If a defective, disease-causing allele is found, is there anything that can be done to prevent or cure the illness? A method to replace missing or defective genes, called **gene therapy,** has been successfully used in a small number of cases. Most gene therapy treatments are still in the experimental stage. One of the main difficulties with gene therapy is inserting a gene into the correct cells and making sure that it functions properly.

1. What is genetic screening?

____

____

____

2. What is the goal of gene therapy?

____

____

3. What are the two main challenges in gene therapy?

____

____

____

Name Period Date

CHAPTER 9 | CONSTRUCTING HISTOGRAMS

Data Analysis Practice

A histogram is a type of bar graph that compares distinct categories of data. The frequency with which data points occur or a percentage of the total number of data points is placed in one of the categories.

Many types of cancer are related to genetic mutations, including a mutation of the BRCA1 gene that has been linked to breast cancer and ovarian cancer in women. The data in the table below shows the incidence of different types of cancers in males and females in the United States during 2002. Each of the values in the table represents the frequency of a particular type of cancer per 100,000 people.

Cancer Incidences in Males and Females

Cancer Type	Males	Females
Bladder	37.0	9.4
Colon	61.3	44.9
Lymphoma (non-Hodgkin)	22.0	15.5
Lung	86.4	53.7
Melanoma	20.9	13.6
Pancreas	12.3	9.5

1. **Synthesize** Construct a histogram that shows the frequency of different types of cancers in males and females.

Name Period Date

2. Analyze How are cancer incidence rates in males and females similar? How are they different?

Name Period Date

DNA FORENSICS: SOLVING A ROYAL MYSTERY

Pre-AP Activity

You have learned in Chapter 9 how repeat sequences in DNA can yield a DNA fingerprint that can be used to identify people. These fingerprints can be generated from nuclear DNA or mitochondrial DNA (mtDNA). One advantage of mtDNA is its maternal pattern of inheritance—because it is passed directly from mothers to offspring of both sexes, it does not undergo recombination. This keeps mtDNA sequences constant over many generations. Brothers and sisters have the same mtDNA as their mother and all maternal relatives and ancestors, allowing relatedness to be traced along distant branches of the maternal family tree.

Evidence from one of the most infamous events of the 20th century—the secret 1918 execution and burial of Tsar Nicholas II of Russia and his household—is presented below. Analyze the evidence presented here to determine the identity of a group of skeletons exhumed in 1991 from a shallow grave in Russia.

IDENTIFYING THE REMAINS

On July 16, 1918, members of the Romanov royal household—Tsar Nicholas II of Russia, his wife, the Tsarina Alexandra, their five children, their family doctor, and three servants—were secretly executed by a Bolshevik firing squad and buried in an undisclosed location. Eyewitness accounts by members of the firing squad later noted that shortly thereafter, the bodies of two of the children were removed from the burial site and cremated.

In 1991, nine skeletons were exhumed from a shallow grave near Ekaterinburg, Russia. Physical characteristics of the skeletons revealed that three of the skeletons belonged to female children; two were from adult females; and four were from adult males. Nuclear DNA samples from the skeletons were taken and compared to determine relatedness among them. The table below shows the five genetic markers that were analyzed for comparison.

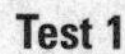

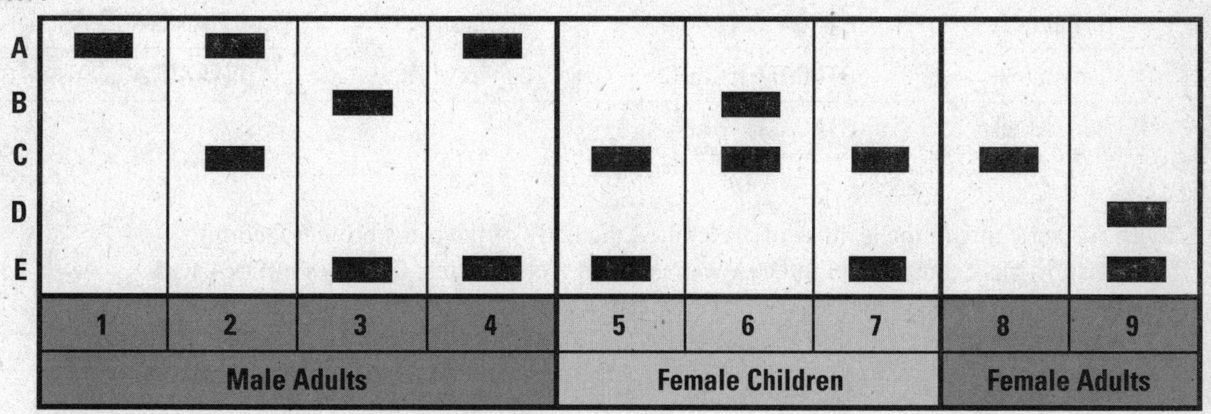

Name Period Date

Answer the following questions on a separate sheet of paper.

1. Look at the DNA markers of the children and compare them to those of the adults. Remembering that offspring get half their DNA from their mother and half from their father, and assuming that the three children share the same parents, determine which two adults could have been the parents of the children. Explain your conclusions. (Hint: Look first at the adult females.)

2. Investigators hypothesized that the remains of five individuals were those of the royal family, while the rest belonged to the doctor and servants. To support their hypothesis, mitchondrial DNA from each female skeleton was compared with that of the Tsarina Alexandra's closest living maternal relative—Prince Philip, the Duke of Edinburgh, whose grandmother was the tsarina's sister. At the same time, mtDNA from the male skeletons was compared with that of Tsar Nicholas II's closest living relative—his great grandnephew James, the Duke of Fife.
Compare the simulated DNA sequences in both tests, looking for differences in bases. Do they support the hypothesis that skeletons 3 and 8 are from the tsar and his wife? Explain your answer.

Test 2: Identifying the Tsarina

mtDNA Donor–maternal lineage	Simulated Test Sequence
Skeleton 5	GTACATT...CAGT
Skeleton 6	GTACATT...CAGT
Skeleton 7	GTACATT...CAGT
Skeleton 8	GTACATT...CAGT
Skeleton 9	GTACATT...CAGC
Prince Philip	GTACATT...CAGT

Test 3: Identifying the Tsar

mtDNA Donor–paternal lineage	Simulated Test Sequence
Skeleton 1	CTTAAGCAC...AT
Skeleton 2	CTTAAGTAC...AT
Skeleton 3	TTTAAGTAC...AT
Skeleton 4	CTTAAGTAC...AC
James of Fife	TTTAAGTAC...AT

3. To further confirm the identity of skeleton 3, the body of the tsar's brother Georgij Romanov was exhumed and mtDNA was sampled. As expected, Georgij's mtDNA was a match. Consider the four tests that were performed and summarize how the evidence suggests that the skeletal remains found at Ekaterinburg belong to the murdered Romanovs.

4. Anna Demidova, Tsarina Alexandra's lady-in-waiting, was among those household members murdered in 1918. Can we presume that skeleton 9 is hers? Explain what type of testing would be needed to provide conclusive evidence.

Name Period Date

CHAPTER 9

MEET THE Y CHROMOSOME

Pre-AP Activity

You have learned in Chapter 9 that bioinfomatics is a powerful tool for decoding genomes. Such technology has enabled scientists to take a close look at the "odd couple" of human chromosomes: the X and Y chromosomes. In particular, scientists are very interested in the Y chromosome, which by any measure is unique among human chromosomes.

Y—THE SMALLEST CHROMOSOME

You learned in Chapter 7 that sex determination in humans is governed by the XY system and in Chapter 9 that the *SRY* gene is the testes-determining factor that makes an individual with a Y chromosome a male. Now you will learn more about this unique chromosome.

The Y chromosome is the smallest of the human chromosomes, but this was not always true. Scientists have postulated that the X and Y chromosomes evolved from a pair of homologous chromosomes, autosomes of the same size that carried the same genes and exhibited crossing over with each other. After the master sex-determining gene *SRY* evolved about 300 million years ago, the chromosome with the *SRY* gene became the Y chromosome. The chromosome without the *SRY* gene became the X. The Y then began to lose some of the genes it shared with the X chromosome. Scientists estimate that about five genes have been lost every million years, and that only about 27 of the original genes remain. Does this hypothesized scenario mean that the Y chromosome will become extinct within a few million years?

WHAT DOES THE Y CHROMOSOME CONSIST OF?

Work done by Dr. David Page of the Massachusetts Institute of Technology (MIT) indicates that the Y is here to stay. The genetic sequence of a Y chromosome was determined in 2003. Page found that the human Y chromosome currently carries 78 genes, many of which are duplicates. These 78 genes code for 27 proteins. The DNA sequence has also revealed that the Y chromosome is highly unique and consists of three types of base sequences.

GROUP 1: About 10 to 15 percent of the base sequences are almost identical to those of the X chromosome. They probably evolved when a large piece of the X chromosome became attached backwards to the Y chromosome about 3–4 million years ago. Only two genes have been identified in this group.

GROUP 2: About 20 percent are more distantly related to the X chromosome and seem to be remnants of the ancestor chromosome from which the X and Y chromosomes evolved. These areas are believed to have evolved as the frequency of crossing over decreased, mutations accumulated, and the X and Y became more different. There are 27 genes in this kind of sequence.

GROUP 3: The remainder of the 50 million bases that make up the Y chromosome consists of long sequences called palindromes that are unique to the Y. A palindrome is a sequence that reads the same forward and backward but in opposite directions, such as the name "Hannah" and the sentence "Madam, I'm Adam." These base sequences contain many genes, both functional and nonfunctional, and are found in multiple copies. Up to 35 copies of some of these genes have been identified. Most likely, many of these palindromic sequences were originally part of other chromosomes that became attached to the Y and then accumulated mutations over millions of years.

Name Period Date

REPAIRING DAMAGE

Whenever cells divide, errors occur. Homologous chromosomes come in pairs, so a cell always has at least one correct copy of a gene. As the Y chromosome evolved, it lost much of its ability to recombine with the X chromosome. Only a small region at the end of the modern X chromosome can cross over with the Y; 95 percent of the Y is male-specific and has no match with the X. Scientists believed that this lack of X-Y crossing over will lead to an accumulation of mutations and cause many sex-specific genes to become nonfunctional. A nonfunctional gene is a lost gene. Since the 22 pairs of autosomes have a repair mechanism for eliminating error, Dr. Page and his team thought that the Y also must have some kind of repair system.

They discovered that the Y, indeed, has a repair system. In this system, palindromes allow the Y to pair up with itself. The presence of palindromes in the two strands of DNA means that each gene in the palindrome has two copies, one on each arm of the sequence. The sequence of the copy of the gene on one arm of the palindrome pairs with the sequence of the copy of the gene on the other arm and corrects errors. Thus, when DNA divides before meiosis in sperm production, genes on the Y chromosome can make repairs by copying the correct sequence from the back-up copy. Apparently, not all errors are deleted, however. The 27 genes that the Y still shares with the X often do not function on the Y. This means that the Y is still evolving and losing genes.

1. What is it about the Y chromosome that suggests that it will not go extinct despite its pattern of losing genes?

____

____

2. Calculate approximately how many genes are found on the X chromosome. Use the information given.

____

____

3. What evidence suggests that the X and Y chromosomes evolved from a common chromosome ancestor?

____

4. The Y chromosome began to evolve about the same time the evolutionary lineage of mammals began to diverge from the lineage of birds. Would you expect birds to have an XY pattern of sex determination? Explain.

____

____

Name Period Date

CHAPTER 9 | FRONTIERS OF BIOTECHNOLOGY

Vocabulary Practice

restriction enzyme
gel electrophoresis
restriction map
polymerase chain reaction (PCR)
primer
DNA fingerprint
clone
genetic engineering
recombinant DNA
plasmid
transgenic
gene knockout
genomics
gene sequencing
Human Genome Project
bioinformatics
DNA microarray
proteomics
genetic screening
gene therapy

A. Stepped-Out Vocabulary Define each word. Then write two additional facts that are related to the word.

WORD	DEFINITION	MORE INFORMATION
Example plasmid	*closed loop of DNA separate from bacterial chromosome*	*can replicate on its own*
		used for making recombinant DNA
1. clone		
2. genomics		
3. genetic screening		
4. DNA microarray		
5. proteomics		

B. Situational Vocabulary Circle the letter of the situation that most closely relates to each vocabulary word.

1. **gene therapy:** a) buying a bicycle; b) replacing a flat bicycle tire
2. **gene sequencing:** a) reading a book's table of contents; b) summarizing a book in a report
3. **gel electrophoresis:** a) counting out 100 pennies; b) sorting coins by value
4. **polymerase chain reaction:** a) division; b) multiplication
5. **clone:** a) a photocopy; b) a fragrance for men
6. **DNA fingerprint:** a) a group yearbook picture; b) a driver's license picture
7. **primer:** a) a referee's whistle to start a game; b) the horn at the end of a game
8. **bioinformatics:** a) searching the index of your biology textbook; b) reading your biology textbook from beginning to end

C. Analogy Vocabulary Set On one blank line next to each vocabulary word, write the letter and number of the definition that best matches. On the other blank line, write the letter and number of the analogy that best matches.

DEFINITIONS	WORD	ANALOGIES
D1. Testing DNA to determine a person's risk of having a genetic disorder	**1.** Human Genome Project ____ ____	**A1.** A surgeon's scalpel
D2. An enzyme that cuts DNA at a specific nucleotide sequence	**2.** plasmid ____ ____	**A2.** Bending a garden hose to stop the flow of water
D3. The study of genomes, within and across species	**3.** restriction enzyme ____ ____	**A3.** A computer virus
D4. A gene that is "turned off" to study its function	**4.** genetic screening ____ ____	**A4.** Alphabetizing all of the movies ever made
D5. Its goals are to map and sequence all human DNA and to identify all genes in the sequence	**5.** gene knockout ____ ____	**A5.** Learning and comparing two similar languages
D6. Closed loop of DNA separate from bacterial DNA that can replicate on its own	**6.** genomics ____ ____	**A6.** Taking a standardized test

D. Vector Vocabulary Define the words in the boxes. On the line across each arrow, write a phrase that describes how the words in the boxes are related to each other.

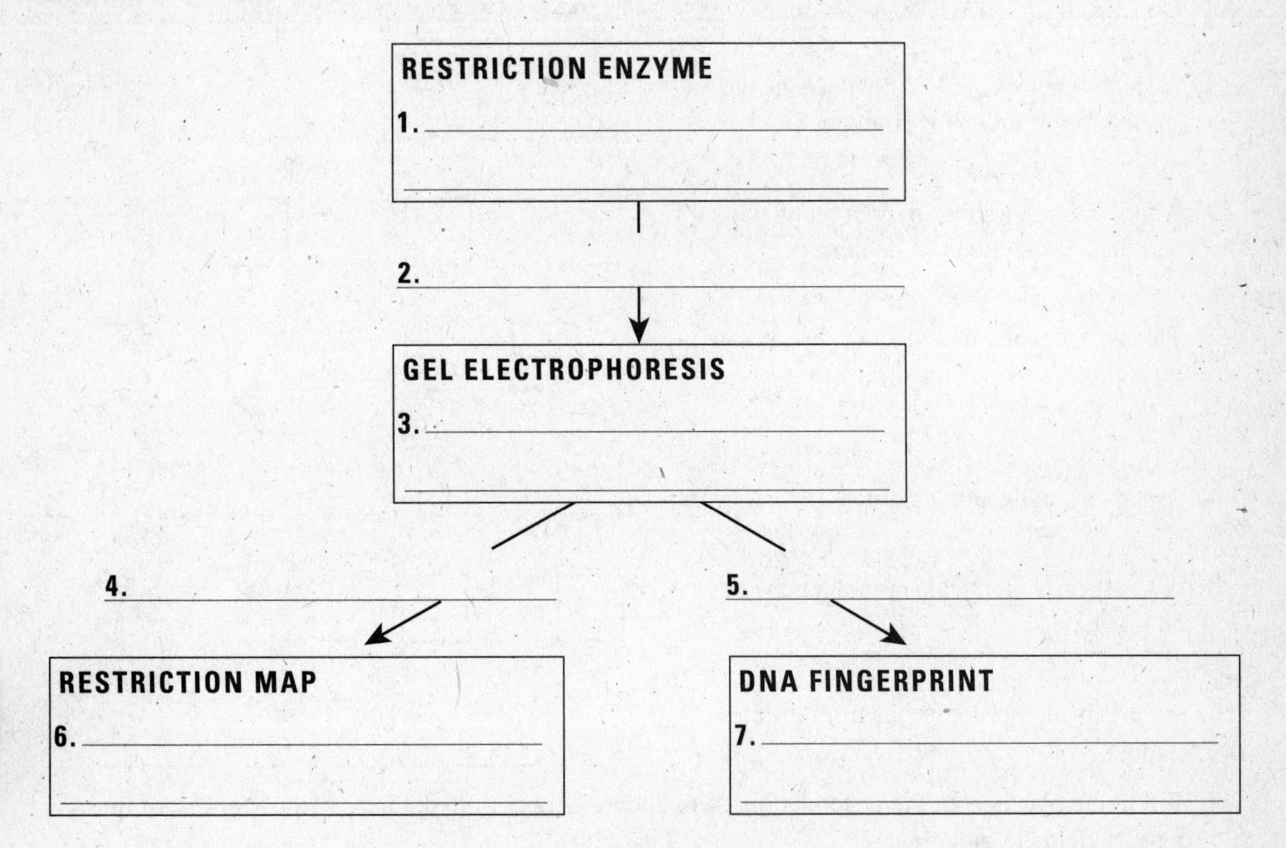

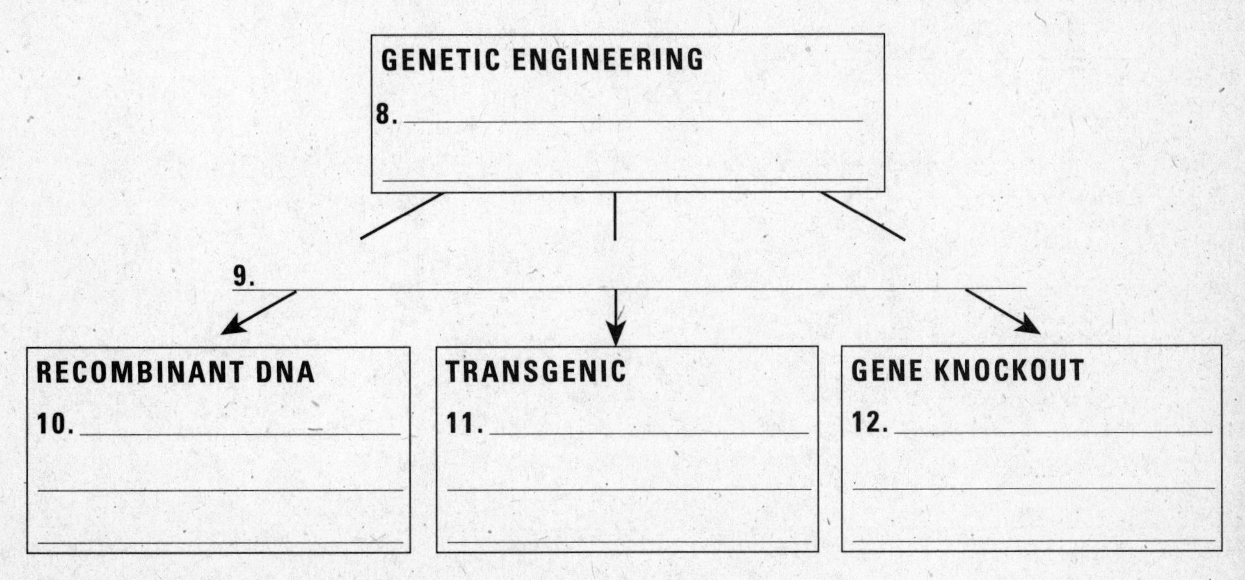

E. Secret Message Next to each definition, fill in the blanks with the vocabulary word that best fits each description. When complete, write the boxed letters in the blanks at the bottom of the page. Then unscramble them to reveal one of the newest fields in biology.

1. A short segment of DNA that acts as the starting point for a new strand of DNA

2. A tool that allows the study of many genes, and their interactions, at one time

3. The experimental treatment of diseases by replacing faulty or missing genes

4. A person's molecular identity

5. A genetically identical copy of a gene or an organism

6. An organism that has genes from different organisms in its genome

Fill in the blanks with the boxed letters from above. Unscramble the letters to reveal one of the newest fields in biology:

___ ___ ___ ___ ___ ___ ___ ___ ___ ___

Name Period Date

UNIT 3

INTERPRETING A PEDIGREE

Unit Project

Pedigree analysis has provided valuable insights into the inheritance of many traits and disorders that occur in humans. The pedigree method is a convenient means of studying and predicting the mode of inheritance of a particular trait. In this project, you will select for analysis a prepared pedigree of a specific genetic disorder. You will research and discuss the disorder and the sample pedigree and determine how the information is used in genetic counseling. You will analyze and describe the pedigree and create a three-panel storyboard that explains your results.

- Your teacher will provide a list of human genetic disorders and a sample pedigree for each disorder. You will choose one of the sample pedigrees for analysis.
- Research the disorder you have chosen. In particular, you will need to know its mode of inheritance, such as autosomal dominant or X-linked recessive.
- Write a one-page summary of what you have learned about the disorder, including details that provide human interest, such as how the disorder is diagnosed and treated, or what life is like living with the disorder.
- Research pedigrees to find out how they can be used to counsel couples who are thinking about having children. What are the qualifications of a genetic counselor? What are the indicators that would lead a couple to seek genetic counseling? Write a summary of your findings.
- Duplicate your sample pedigree on the center panel of your storyboard. You may use colored markers, construction paper, or a creative idea of your own. Be sure all symbols and labels are correct. Provide a key to the symbols, and post it on your storyboard. Title your pedigree appropriately.
- Post your one-page summary of the genetic disorder you have researched on your storyboard along with your summary of genetic counseling and how it is used.
- For each generation in your pedigree, write a description of the genotypes and phenotypes of its members. You may label each individual of a generation with his or her genotype directly on the pedigree. Then write a short explanation for each. You may show how you infer certain unknown genotypes by using a Punnett square or by explaining the existing symbols. Post your explanations on the storyboard in such a way that the generation to which the explanation belongs is obvious.
- In your research and storyboard preparation, be sure the following questions are answered:
    1. How can a family pedigree be useful when discussing your medical history with a doctor?
    2. Under what conditions of inheritance can a pedigree predict with 100 percent certainty what the genotype of an offspring will be?
- Be as creative as possible, and be sure your storyboard is neat, organized, and easy to follow.

On the following page you will find the evaluation rubric. Points will be assigned according to how well a task is done, as well as whether you have fully or only partially completed a task. Any task left undone will be assigned a zero. Your teacher will provide a timetable for this project.

Name Period Date

Interpreting a Pedigree Evaluation Rubric

Requirements	Maximum Points	Earned Points (teacher to fill in)
Pedigree is accurately reproduced on the storyboard, includes all symbols and labels, and has an appropriate and descriptive title.	5	
Accurate key to pedigree symbols and labels is clearly posted on the storyboard.	5	
Summary describes the disorder, how it is inherited, its manner of diagnosis and treatment, and its effect on a person's lifestyle.	20	
Storyboard describes the qualifications and work of a genetic counselor, why people might seek genetic counseling, and the benefits of pedigree analysis.	10	
Genotype of each member in each generation is clearly labeled.	10	
Descriptions of each individual's genotype and phenotype are provided, including a rationale or probability calculation for unknown genotypes, such as a Punnett square.	10	
Explanations of each genotype within a generation are posted on the storyboard and clearly associated with a specific generation.	10	
A thorough understanding of the relationships of parents, offspring, and generations is evident in the overall presentation.	10	
Two required questions are answered either in a separate post on the storyboard or are included in the summary.	10	
Answers are well reasoned, stated, and supported.	5	
Storyboard is neat, organized, and easy to follow.	5	
Rubric Score:	100 points	
Extra Credit (given at teacher's discretion):		
A well-known person who is affected with the disorder is described.	5	
	Total Score:	
Teacher's Comments:		

UNIT 3 | INTERPRETING A PEDIGREE

Unit Project Teacher Notes

Purpose: Understand, prepare, and interpret a pedigree, and explain how it can be used as a diagnostic model.

Overview: Students will prepare and interpret a model pedigree storyboard using appropriate symbols. Students will

- research a specific assigned genetic trait and a provided pedigree
- reproduce the pedigree on a three-panel, freestanding storyboard
- describe and explain the symbols and markers of interest in each generation
- clearly identify the trait and describe its mode of inheritance, using dialogue boxes posted on the storyboard

Preparation:

- Copy the project description and the rubric for students.
- Plan timetable.
- Select several traits from the list below, or use others if you prefer. If any of your students are affected by one of the disorders below, you may wish to avoid using that disorder.

Recessive Traits	Dominant Traits
albinism	achondroplasia (dwarfism)
color blindness (X-linked)	brachydactyly
cystic fibrosis	FSH muscular dystrophy
Duchenne's muscular dystrophy (X-linked)	Huntington's disease
hemophilia (X-linked)	night blindness (possible X-linked)
phenylketonuria	osteogenesis imperfecta IV (brittle-bone disease)
sickle-cell anemia	

- Obtain information about each disorder you have selected, including a model pedigree diagram. Allow students to select a diagram they wish to research. Website resources are plentiful for pedigree diagrams and their analyses. Go to **ClassZone.com** for helpful resources and links.
- To simplify student research, you may wish to prepare a student handout that summarizes the meanings of all the symbols that may be included in a pedigree.

Project Management:

- Assign the project at the beginning of Chapter 6.
- Read over and discuss the project sheet before students choose a topic.
- Projects are completed outside of class and should take three weeks to complete.
- Projects may be done individually.

- Because of sensitivity issues and assessment difficulties, students should be discouraged from doing a personal pedigree.
- Have students check in weekly to monitor their progress.
- Answers to the questions in the sixth bulleted item of the student project page:
  1. Having a family pedigree helps a doctor identify inheritance patterns and determine if you are at risk for developing a certain disease.
  2. A pedigree can successfully predict a genotype of a specific offspring with 100 percent accuracy only in cases where both parents have the same homozygous genotype.

Differentiation: This project can be adapted for various ability levels within the class.

- **Below Level students:** Restrict research to autosomal dominant pedigrees. You may also wish to reduce the pedigree to two generations.
- **Pre-AP students:** Ask students to include information about recent advancements in gene therapy for the treatment of the disorder they have selected. Alternatively, have students relate information about early detection of the disorder in a fetus.

Answer Key

Section 6.1

Study Guide

1. somatic/body cells; germ cells/gametes
2. in the reproductive organs; ovaries and testes
3. 46

4. mother
5. father
6. autosomes
7. X
8. Y

9. female
10. Y chromosome

11. They fuse together.
12. gametes
13. 23
14. 22; 1

15. *Mitosis* makes diploid cells; *Meiosis:* makes haploid cells; *Mitosis:* makes genetically identical cells; *Meiosis:* makes genetically unique cells; *Mitosis:* happens throughout lifetime; *Meiosis:* happens at specific times in an organism's life cycle; *Mitosis:*involved in asexual reproduction; *Meiosis:* involved in sexual reproduction

16. a pair of chromosomes, one from the mother and one from the father, that have the same genes, length, and overall appearance
17. autosome: chromosome that directs the body's development of traits not directly related to sexual characteristics; somatic cell: body cell

Power Notes

Somatic cells: also called body cells, make up most of the body tissues and organs, not passed on to children

Gametes: sex cells, passed on to children

1. autosomes: chromosomes that contain genes not directly related to the sex of an organism
2. homologous chromosomes: pair of chromosomes, inherit one from each parent, carry the same genes although the genes may code for different traits
3. sex chromosomes: contain genes that directly control the development of sexual characteristics

Diploid cell: has two copies of each chromosomes, one from mother and one from father; body cells typically diploid, result from mitosis

Haploid cell: has one copy of each chromosome; gametes typically haploid, result from meiosis

Mitosis: makes genetically identical cells, makes diploid cells, takes place throughout organism's lifetime, involved in asexual reproduction

Meiosis: makes genetically unique cells, makes haploid cells, takes place at certain times in life cycle, involved in sexual reproduction

Reinforcement

1. Gametes are located in the reproductive organs and are haploid. Somatic cells make up the tissues and organs of the body and are diploid.
2. Homologous chromosomes look the same and carry the same genes.
3. Meiosis is a process that creates haploid cells. Fertilization fuses two haploid cells to make a diploid cell.

Section 6.2

Study Guide

1. sister chromatid
2. homologous chromosomes

3. Refer to Figure 6.5 for visual answers. prophase I
4. metaphase I
5. anaphase I
6. telophase I
7. prophase II
8. metaphase II
9. anaphase II
10. telophase II

11. anaphase I
12. anaphase II

13. DNA
14. DNA, organelles, molecular building blocks
15. female

Sperm Formation/Egg Formation: Refer to Figure 6.6 for visual answers.

16. Gametogenesis is the "birth" or formation of gametes.

17. cells produced by meiosis in the female body that contain little more than DNA and are eventually broken down

Power Notes

Homologous chromosomes: pair of chromosomes, inherit one from each parent, carry the same genes although the genes may code for different traits, separate in meiosis I

Sister chromatids: duplicates of each other, each half of a duplicated chromosome, attached together at the centromere, separate in meiosis II

1. prophase I: chromosomes condense, homologous chromosomes begin to pair up, nuclear envelope breaks down, spindle fibers form
2. metaphase I: spindle fibers align homologous chromosomes along the cell equator
3. anaphase I: homologous chromosomes separate to opposite sides of cell, sister chromatids remain attached together
4. telophase I: spindle fibers fall apart, nuclear membrane may form again, cell undergoes cytokinesis
5. prophase II: nuclear envelope breaks down if necessary, spindle fibers form
6. metaphase II: spindle fibers align chromosomes along the cell equator
7. anaphase II: chromatids separate to opposite sides of cell
8. telophase II: nuclear membranes form around chromosomes, chromosomes begin to uncoil, spindle fibers fall apart, cell undergoes cytokinesis

Reinforcement

1. anaphase I
2. anaphase II

Section 6.3

Study Guide

1. the study of biological inheritance patterns and variation in organisms
2. Gregor Mendel
3. Mendel recognized that traits are inherited as discrete units, whereas many others believed that traits were mixed together.
4. control over breeding; removed the stamens and fertilized the pistil with pollen from a pea plant of his choice
5. use of purebred plants; used self-pollinating, purebred pea plants
6. studied "either-or" traits; looked at traits that did not have intermediate characteristics such as pea shape, pea color, flower color, pod shape, pod color, flower position, and plant height
7. Pea plants reproduce quickly, and he could control how they mate.
8. **Box 2:** Allowed F_1 offspring to self-pollinate. **Box 4:** Calculated the phenotypic ratios in the F_2 generation.
9. genes
10. Organisms inherit two copies of each gene, one from each parent. Genes segregate during gamete formation, so organisms donate only one copy of each gene in their gametes.
11. the discrete units, or genes; the result of the separation of chromosomes during meiosis
12. a genetically uniform line of organisms

Power Notes

Three key choices: control over breeding, use of purebred plants, observation of "either-or" traits that appeared in two forms

Pea plant characteristics: pea shape, pea color, flower color, pod shape, pod color, flower position, plant height

Cross: the mating of two organisms; Mendel mated purebred pea plants with purple flowers with purebred flowers

P: the parental generation; Mendel used purebred plants for the P generation; for example, he crossed purebred plants with purple flowers with purebred plants with white flowers

F_1: the first generation of offspring resulting from the parental cross; for example, Mendel's F_1 plants all had purple flowers; Mendel allowed this generation to self-pollinate

F_2: the second generation; the result of the self-pollination of F_1 plants; for example, in Mendel's F_2 generation, 3/4 had purple flowers and 1/4 had white flowers

Results: For all seven traits, Mendel found that approximately 3/4 of F_2 offspring had one trait and 1/4 of the offspring had the other trait

Conclusions: traits are inherited as discrete units (genes), *law of segregation*— inherit two copies of each gene, donate only one copy of each gene in gametes

Reinforcement

1. F_2
2. the two copies of each gene that are present in organisms; during gamete formation, or meiosis (anaphase I)

Section 6.4

Study Guide

1. genes code for proteins
2. any of the alternative forms of a gene that may occur at a specific locus
3. homozygous; heterozygous
4. Homologous chromosomes are two chromosomes, one from the mother and one from the father, that have the same length, overall appearance, and genes, although the alleles may differ.

   Homologous Chromosomes: Images should be similar to the Visual Vocab on page 180 in the textbook. Students will label Gene A, Gene A, gene B, and Gene b.
5. Answers will vary. Sample answer: Genotype is the underlying genetics of an organism, which could be compared to someone's thoughts that you can't read. Phenotype is the observable traits, which could be compared to someone's words that tell you what they're thinking about.
6. as letters, uppercase for dominant alleles and lowercase for recessive alleles
7. **Genotype:** homozygous dominant; homozygous recessive; heterozygous. **Phenotype:** dominant; recessive; dominant. **Alleles:** TT; tt; Tt
8. Yes, it has to be homozygous recessive.
9. environment, such as nutrients and sunshine
10. homozygous dominant
11. allele
12. heterozygous; recessive

Power Notes

Gene: piece of DNA that tells a cell to make a certain polypeptide;

Allele: an alternate form of a gene; there may be many different forms of the same gene in a population; each individual organism has only two forms of that gene, one from the mother and one from the father

Genome: all of an organism's genetic material, unique;

Genotype: the genetic makeup of a specific set of genes; may be homozygous dominant, homozygous recessive, or heterozygous

Homozygous: describes two alleles at the same locus that are the same

Heterozygous: describes two alleles at the same locus that are different

Symbols: represented with individual letters; uppercase letter = dominant; lowercase letter = recessive

Dominant: expressed even when two alleles are different;

Recessive: expressed only when two copies are present

Phenotype: an organism's physical characteristics or traits; influenced by genotype and environmental factors

Reinforcement

1. The phenotype would be like the building made from the blueprints.
2. Bb; bb; BB

Section 6.5

Study Guide

1. parent's alleles/genotype
2. parent's alleles/genotype
3. possible genotypes of offspring
4. because the alleles segregated during gamete formation (meiosis) when the homologous chromosomes separated
5. a comparison that tells the proportion of offspring that have a particular genotype; a comparison that tells the proportion of offspring that have a particular phenotype
6. 1:2:1
7. 3:1
8. a cross that examines the inheritance of two different traits
9. Figure 6.17 represents a dihybrid cross. Each parent organism has two alleles for both traits, which makes a total of four alleles.
10. AB, Ab
11. 9:3:3:1
12. average, exact
13. multiply
14. one-fourth
15. a cross between an organism with the recessive phenotype and an organism with an unknown genotype
16. Allele pairs are independent. They separate independently of each other during gamete formation (meiosis).

Power Notes

Punnett square: grid system for predicting possible genotypes resulting from a cross; *Axes:* represent possible gamete genotypes of each parent; *Grid boxes:* show all possible genotypes of offspring

Monohybrid cross: examines the inheritance of one specific trait; students may choose to sketch a Punnett square for a specific cross

Ratios: predicted genotypic and phenotypic ratios can be determined from a Punnett square; specific ratios will vary based on example Punnett square used

Testcross: cross between an organism with the recessive phenotype (homozygous recessive genotype) and an organism with the dominant phenotype but an unknown genotype; looking at the offspring allows you to figure out the phenotype of the dominant organism

Dihybrid cross: examines the inheritance of two traits; students may choose to sketch a Punnett square for a specific cross

Ratios: predicted genotypic and phenotypic ratios can be determined from a Punnett square; specific ratios will vary based on example Punnett square used

Law of independent assortment: developed by Mendel as a result of examining dihybrid crosses; determined that the inheritance of one trait does not influence the inheritance of a second trait

Probability: the likelihood that a particular event will happen; predicts the average number of occurrences; the distribution of genes in gametes and the fertilization of a particular egg by a particular sperm are random events whose outcome can be predicted with probability

Reinforcement

1. monohybrid
2. 1:1 for heterozygous:homozygous recessive
3. 1:1 for dominant:recessive

Section 6.6

Study Guide

1. independent assortment of chromosomes during meiosis and random fertilization of gametes
2. new combinations of alleles
3. Unique genetic combinations result in organisms with unique phenotypes, which increases the likelihood that some will survive under changing conditions.
4. duplicated

Crossing Over sketch: Refer to Figure 6.20 for visual answers.

Box 1: Each cell should contain one large duplicated chromosome and one small duplicated chromosome. One sister chromatid on each chromosome should appear to have undergone crossing over. **Box 2:** Each cell should contain one large chromosome and one small chromosome. The exact combination of chromosomes will depend on how the students divided the chromosomes.

5. Yes. The chromosomes carrying those genes will line up randomly and separate randomly during meiosis.
6. Yes. The genes will be far enough from each other that crossing over is very likely to occur between them.
7. No. The genes are likely to be linked and to travel together during meiosis.

8. crossing over
9. genetic linkage

Power Notes

Fertilization: random; increases unique combinations of genes; in humans, the chance of getting any one combination of chromosomes from any one set of parents is one out of $2^{23} \times 2^{23}$, which is one out of over 64 trillion combinations

Meiosis: Independent assortment of chromosomes: increases unique combinations of genes; homologous chromosomes pair randomly along the cell equator; in human cells, about 2^{23}, or 8 million, different combinations of chromosomes could result

Crossing over: exchange of chromosomes segments between homologous chromosomes during prophase I of meiosis I; creates new combinations of genes; recombined chromosomes are a combination of genes from both the mother and the father

Figure should look similar to Figure 6.20.

Genetic linkage: genes located close together on same chromosome tend to be inherited together; crossing over less likely to occur between genes located close together; not found by Mendel because he studied traits on separate chromosomes or traits located far apart on the same chromosome; means that not all genes follow the law of independent assortment

Reinforcement

1. independent assortment of chromosomes, random fertilization, crossing over
2. the exchange of chromosome segments between homologous chromosomes
3. No. The two genes are unlikely to be separated by crossing over, so they will be inherited together.

Chapter 6

Data Analysis Practice

1. brown; white
2. Answers will vary but should include a testable hypothesis based on the observations such as the alleles for brown hair are dominant over all other alleles for hair color.

Pre-AP* Activity

VIEWING MENDEL THROUGH A MODERN LENS

1. A recessive allele does not vary from one generation to another because the DNA that makes up the gene does not change from one generation to the next. (Note that Mendel is not allowing for mutations.)
2. Heterozygous offspring that result from the cross of one dominant heterozygous parent and one recessive homozygous parent carry one allele from each parent. The sex of the parent does affect the way the genes are distributed. (Mendel knew this because heterozygous parents of this generation had an equal chance of passing on either of these alleles to their offspring.)
3. Mendel is considering the cross of two heterozygous

plants. There are four combinations of alleles possible in the ratio of 1:2:1: one homozygous dominant (AA), two heterozygous dominant (Aa), and one homozygous recessive (aa). The alleles sort independently, so all four possibilities are equally likely.

4. Mendel is suggesting that genotypes be written with the allele from the male gamete first and the allele from the female gamete second. (This shows the equal contribution of one allele from each parent in the zygote.)
5. Allele pairs separate independently of each other during gamete formation. The presence of one trait does not affect the presence of another. This is Mendel's law of independent assortment.

Pre-AP Activity

CHI SQUARE TESTS

1. $P(1) = 9/16$ or 0.5625, $P(2) = 3/16$ or 0.1875, $P(3) = 3/16$ or 0.1875, $P(4) = 1/16$ or 0.0625; $E(1) = 313$, $E(2) = 104$, $E(3) = 104$, $E(4) = 35$
2. 0.511. Yes. Since the observed value of χ^2 is less than the critical value in the table (7.81), we can conclude that the expected and actual results are close enough to not be coincidental.

Vocabulary Practice

A. Situational Vocabulary

1. a
2. b
3. a
4. b
5. a
6. a
7. a
8. a
9. b
10. b
11. b
12. a

B. The Same But Different

1. Both describe chromosomes in sexually reproducing organisms. Autosomes carry genes for traits not directly related to the sex of an organism. Sex chromosomes carry genes for traits directly related to the sex of an organism.
2. Both are types of cells found in sexually reproducing organisms. Somatic cells are diploid body cells. Gametes are haploid reproductive cells.
3. Both are types of gametes. Sperm are produced by male organisms and male parts of organisms. Eggs are produced by females and female parts of organisms.
4. Both describe genotype. Homozygous describes an organism that has two alleles of the same type. Heterozygous describes an organism that has two alleles that are different.
5. Both describe a characteristic of some alleles. Dominant alleles are expressed when both alleles are dominant or when only one allele is dominant. Recessive alleles are expressed only when both alleles are recessive.
6. Both describe how many sets of chromosomes are present in a cell. Diploid cells have two sets of chromosomes. Haploid cells have one set of chromosomes.
7. Both examine the inheritance of a trait or traits resulting from crosses between organisms. Monohybrid crosses examine the inheritance of only one trait. Dihybrid crosses examine the inheritance of two traits.

C. Complete the Story

1. traits, genetic, purebred, crossed
2. law of segregation, gene, gametogenesis, law of independent assortment, crossing over, genetic linkage

D. Vector Vocabulary

1. a sequence of DNA that codes for a polypeptide
2. genes and alleles are basically the same, but a gene is more generic and an allele is a more specific form of a gene
3. any of multiple forms of a gene
4. alleles influence phenotype
5. the physical appearance of an organism
6. alleles may be expressed or hidden

7. an allele that is expressed even if an organism only has one copy of it
8. an allele that is expressed only if an organism has two copes of it
9. combinations of alleles make up genotype
10. the genes/alleles that make up an organism
11. examples of genotype
12. two alleles that are the same
13. two alleles that are different

Section 7.1

Study Guide

1. chromosomes that determine an organism's sex
2. all other chromosomes; do not directly affect an organism's sex
3. a carrier does not show symptoms of a disorder but can pass the disorder to offspring

   Autosomal Recessive: DD, no disorder; Dd, carrier; Dd, carrier; dd, disorder.
   Autosomal Dominant: DD, disorder; Dd, disorder; Dd, disorder; dd, no disorder

4. genes that are located on the sex chromosomes

   Sex Chromosome Inheritance: XX, female; XX, female; XY, male; XY, male

5. A female can only pass on X chromosomes, but a male can pass on either X or Y chromosomes.
6. male characteristics
7. Males show the phenotypes from all sex-linked genes; females exhibit phenotypes similarly to autosomal gene expression, except for X chromosome inactivation.
8. A carrier is a person who "transports" a disease-causing allele to offspring.
9. In females, one of the two X chromosomes in every cell is randomly "turned off."

Power Notes

Autosomes— all chromosomes other than sex chromosomes; do not directly determine an organism's sex
Autosomal gene expression— two alleles that interact to produce a phenotypic trait;
Inheritance of autosomes—Punnett square should demonstrate that inheritance occurs according to Mendel's rules, one allele from each parent
Sex chromosomes — chromosomes that determine an organism's sex;
Inheritance of sex chromosomes — Punnett square should indicate that females (XX) can only pass on an X chromosome and males (XY) can pass on either chromosome;
Expression in males — all sex-linked genes are expressed because there is no second allele that could mask the first allele;
Expression in females — similar to autosomal, but one X chromosome in each cell is randomly "turned off" through X chromosome inactivation

Reinforcement

1. Two copies of a gene can both affect phenotype.
2. A carrier has one normal, dominant allele and one recessive, disease-causing allele, and does not have the disorder but can pass it on.
3. genes on the sex chromosomes
4. Males will express all sex-linked genes because they have only one copy of each gene. Females express sex-linked genes similar to autosomal genes. However, one X chromosome in each cell is randomly turned off.

Section 7.2

Study Guide

1. In incomplete dominance neither allele is completely dominant and one allele is not hidden in a heterozygote. The heterozygous phenotype is somewhere between the homozygous phenotypes.
2. In codominance both alleles are completely expressed and the heterozygous phenotype contains the separate products of both alleles.
3. a trait for which a gene has more than two alleles

4. third, distinct phenotype; neither of the homozygous parental phenotypes is seen
5. betta fish (green, steel blue, royal blue); 4 o'clock plant (white, red, pink)
6. third phenotype that has both homozygous parental phenotypes
7. blood type (A, B, AB)

   Polygenic traits: traits produced by two or more genes; show continuous ranges of phenotypes; examples include height, eye color, skin color.
   Epistasis: one gene affects the expression of other genes involved in a particular trait; examples include albinism

8. The environment can affect gene expression, which will influence phenotype.
9. Sex determination in sea turtles depends on both genes and the temperature at which sea turtle eggs mature. Human height is affected both by genes and such factors as nutrition and health care.
10. neither allele is dominant
11. both alleles are expressed together
12. Polygenic traits are traits produced by two or more genes.

Power Notes

Incomplete dominance — heterozygous phenotype is intermediate between parental phenotypes; parental phenotypes not seen in F_1 generation; neither allele completely dominant nor completely recessive
Codominance—two alleles fully and separately expressed; both parental phenotypes seen in all F_1 offspring; alleles neither dominant nor recessive
Multiple alleles—genes with more than two alleles
Polygenic traits—traits that result from the interaction of two or more genes
Epistasis—a gene that overshadows all other genes for a particular trait
Environment and genotype— phenotype is often the result of interactions between environment and genotype; temperature and sex of sea turtles; identical twins raised separately

Reinforcement

1. two alleles interact to produce an intermediate phenotype
2. two alleles are both completely and separately expressed
3. a trait produced by two or more genes
4. one gene affects the expression of other genes
5. human height or sex determination of sea turtles

Section 7.3

Study Guide

1. when genes are on the same chromosome and tend to be inherited together
2. Many generations of fruit flies could be quickly and cheaply grown; fruit flies had easily observed traits.
3. Wild type is the most common phenotype; mutant type is a much less common phenotype.
4. Linked genes are on the same chromosome; chromosomes, not genes, assort independently during meiosis; homologous genes can be exchanged through cross-overs during meiosis.

   Punnett and Bateson: studied pea plants; suggested that some genes were linked
   Morgan: studied fruit flies; concluded that linked genes were on the same chromosome; chromosomes assort independently

5. The closer genes are, the more likely they will be inherited together; the farther apart they are, the more likely they are to be separated.
6. the frequency of cross-overs during meiosis was related to the distance between genes
7. a map of the relative locations of genes on a chromosome
8. the percentage of cross-overs is converted into map units (a cross-over frequency of 1 percent is equal to 1 map unit), and gene locations are determined based on all

cross-over frequencies for the genes being mapped

9. relative locations and an estimate of physical distance between genes, but not actual physical distances

Linkage Map:
A—7—D—13—B—5—C

Power Notes

Mendel—crossed pea plants; determined 9:3:3:1 ratios in dihybrid crosses
Conclusions—two alleles for each trait; alleles assort independently;
Punnett and Bateson—crossed pea plants; dihybrid cross ratios differed from 9:3:3:1;
Conclusions—suggested that some traits were linked
Morgan—used fruit flies to determine that linked traits are on the same chromosome
Conclusions—genes cross over during meiosis; chromosomes, not genes, assort independently;
Sturtevant's hypothesis—frequency of cross-overs during meiosis related to distance between genes; the greater the distance, the greater the frequency of cross-overs;
Sturtevant's experiments— studied linked traits in fruit flies; recorded the percentage of times crossing over occurred; used cross-over frequencies to make linkage maps,
Making a linkage map—cross-over frequency converted into map units; 1 percent cross-over equivalent to 1 map unit; by knowing all cross-over frequencies of genes of interest, the relative locations of the genes can be determined; not a map of physical distance between genes

Reinforcement

1. Chromosomes, not genes, assort independently.
2. the closer the genes, the more likely they will be inherited together; the farther apart the genes, the more likely they will be separated by cross-overs during meiosis.
3. a map of the relative locations of genes on a chromosome
4. The percentage of times two genes cross over is equal to the number of map units between the genes.

Section 7.4

Study Guide

1. chromosomes assort independently during meiosis; relationships among alleles are the same
2. inheritance is straight-forward
3. Anyone (male or female) with a recessive disorder-causing allele can pass on the disorder.
4. because males, unlike females, cannot have a normal, dominant allele that would mask the effect of a recessive, disorder-causing allele
5. a chart that traces phenotypes and genotypes in a family
6. Phenotypes are used to infer genotypes.
7. If approximately the same number of males and females show the phenotype, then the gene is most likely autosomal.
8. X^dX^d
   X^dY
   female carrier
   X^DX^d, X^DY; X^DX^D, X^DX^d, X^DY, X^dY
   X^DX^d, X^dY; X^DX^d, X^dX^d, X^DY, X^dY
   X^dX^d, X^DY; X^DX^d, X^dY
   X^dX^d, X^dY; X^dX^d, X^dY
9. karyotypes and genetic testing (genetic screening)
10. It can show any large-scale changes in chromosomes.
11. a picture of all of the chromosomes in a cell

Power Notes

Sex-linked disorders in males— much more frequent than in females; no 2nd X chromosome to mask the one X chromosome present
Sex-linked disorders in females— only evident when both alleles are recessive; can be a carrier
Pedigree—chart for tracing phenotypes and genotypes within a family

Tracing autosomal genes
• equal numbers of males and females
• people with recessive phenotype must be homozygous recessive
• people with dominant phenotype can be either homozygous dominant or heterozygous
• two heterozygotes can have offspring of either phenotype (dominant or recessive) or
• any genotype (homozygous dominant, heterozygous, or homozygous recessive)
Tracing sex-linked genes
• more males than females will exhibit a recessive phenotype; females can be carriers
• females with recessive phenotype have two recessive alleles; males with recessive phenotype have one
• heterozygous females do not show the recessive phenotype, but are carriers
• female carriers can pass on recessive allele to either male or female offspring
• males with recessive phenotype can pass the recessive allele only to female offspring
Karyotype—picture of all chromosomes in a cell
Karyotype shows—large-scale changes in chromosomes

Reinforcement

1. because they will only show a recessive phenotype if they have two recessive alleles
2. a chart used to trace phenotypes and genotypes within a family
3. Equal numbers of males and females will have the recessive phenotype for an autosomal gene, but more males will show a recessive, sex-linked phenotype.

Chapter 7

Data Analysis Practice

1. Students should construct a double bar graph with nine temperatures on the x-axis bars. Number of turtles should be on the y-axis.
2. Temperatures at the extremes of the range appear to have a greater effect on sex determination than temperatures in the middle of the range.

Pre-AP Activity

INCOMPLETE DOMINANCE IN FOUR O'CLOCKS

1. Student diagram of the F_1 self-cross will show one red R_1R_1 flower, one white R_2R_2 flower, and two pink R_1R_2 flowers. A self-cross of each F_2 genotype produces all homozygous red flowers in one Punnett square, all homozygous white flowers in a second Punnett square, and the two self-crosses of heterozygous pink produce the pattern of red, pink, and white flowers in a 1:2:1 ratio.
2. The cross between a homozygous dominant and a homozygous recessive produces a generation of heterozygous offspring with a phenotype that partially expresses the dominant trait. The dominant and recessive phenotypes reappear in the F_2 generation, in a ratio of 1 dominant; 2 incomplete dominant, 1 recessive.
3. The example of the four o'clocks show a blending in the phenotype, not genotype. If inheritance were caused by blending of the heritable factors, or genes, the red and white traits would not have segregated out in the F_2 generation. Once the pink phenotype appeared, all future flowers would have been shades of pink. The fact that red and white phenotypes were produced from pink flowers demonstrates that the heritable factors are discrete units.

Pre-AP Activity

ROYAL HEMOPHILIA

1. Normal. Neither of his parents carried the allele for hemophilia, so he cannot be a carrier nor a hemophilic.
2. Alexis's sisters each had a 1 in 2 chance of being a carrier. Their mother was a carrier, which means that half of her children would be expected to have the hemophilia allele. The

probability that all four daughters were carriers is 1 in 16 (1/2 x 1/2 x 1/2 x 1/2).

3. Zero. Alexis's daughters all would have been carriers because they would have inherited Alexis's defective allele and one of the dominant alleles of the mother.

4. Yes. A female can inherit hemophilia if she has a hemophilic father and a mother who is either a carrier or hemophilic.

5. The probability is zero. There are no carriers or hemophilics in the present or previous generation of the British royal family.

Vocabulary Practice

A. Compound Word Puzzle

1. sex-linked genes; expressed differently in males and females

2. linkage map; based on cross-over frequencies

3. X chromosome inactivation; females are a patchwork of cells

4. pedigree; phenotypes used to infer genotypes

5. polygenic trait; examples include eye color, skin color, and height

6. incomplete dominance; third, distinct phenotype in which homozygous phenotypes are not seen

B. Words in Context

1. satellite weather map

2. cranberry-raspberry juice

3. power failure

4. trace genes in a family

5. two people talking

6. ferry crossing a lake

7. general idea

8. basketball team

C. Do-It Yourself Matching

1. Sample answer: a gene on a sex chromosome

2. Sample answer: two alleles interact to produce a phenotype between the two homozygous phenotypes

3. Sample answer: a person who does not have a disorder but can pass it on

4. Sample answer: a map of the relative locations of genes on a chromosome

5. Sample answer: both alleles of a gene are fully and separately expressed

6. Sample answer: a picture of all chromosomes

D. Who Am I?

1. X chromosome inactivation

2. codominance

3. pedigree

4. karyotype

5. incomplete dominance

6. carrier

7. linkage map

8. polygenic trait

E. Find the Odd Word

1. X chromosome inactivation; the other terms refer to maps of chromosomes

2. polygenic trait; the other terms are connected to the expression of genetic disorders in males and females

3. linkage map; the other two terms are types of interactions between two alleles

4. incomplete dominance; the other two terms are related to methods of investigating human genetics

F. Analogies

1. carrier

2. incomplete dominance

3. X chromosome inactivation

4. karyotype

5. polygenic trait

6. codominance

7. linkage map

8. Sample answer: painting a baby's room pink for a daughter or blue for a son

9. Sample answer: tracing a tree's root system

Section 8.1

Study Guide

1. Mice lived

2. Mice died

3. Mice lived

4. Mice died

5. the S form

6. Griffith concluded that a transforming principle had been transferred from the heat-killed S bacteria to the live R bacteria.

7. **Result:** DNA is present, but protein is not. **Avery's Question:** What is the chemical makeup of the transforming principle? **Result:** enzymes that destroy DNA

8. sulfur, phosphorus

9. phosphorus, sulfur

10. **Experiment 1:** sulfur; radioactivity absent. **Experiment 2:** phosphorus; radioactivity present

11. A bacteriophage is a virus that infects bacteria. It consists of a DNA molecule surrounded by a protein coat.

Power Notes

Griffith's experiments: Injected bacteria into mice and noted that the S type killed mice, but the R type did not. Killed the S bacteria with heat and injected them into mice. Did not kill the mice. Mixed heat-killed S bacteria with live R bacteria and injected them into mice. Killed the mice. Found live S bacteria.
Conclusion: A "transforming principle" was transferred from the heat-killed S bacteria to the R bacteria.

Avery's experiments: purified the transforming principle described in Griffith's experiments and conduced three tests; Qualitative tests that showed DNA was present; not protein Chemical analyses that showed that the proportion of elements matched the proportion of elements in DNA, not protein; Enzyme tests that showed that enzymes that destroyed proteins and RNA did not affect transforming principle. Enzymes that destroyed DNA destroyed the ability of transforming principle to function.
Conclusion: DNA is the transforming principle

Hershey and Chase's experiments: used bacteriophages grown in either radioactive sulfur (component of proteins) or radioactive phosphorus (component of DNA); bacteriophages are viruses that infect bacteria and take over the cell's genetic machinery to make more viruses
Experiment 1: infected bacteria with bacteriophages grown in radioactive sulfur; separated bacteria from bacteriophages; found no significant radioactivity in the bacteria
Experiment 2: infected bacteria with bacteriophages grown in radioactive phosphorus; separated bacteria from bacteriophages; found significant radioactivity inside the bacteria, which showed that DNA from the bacteriophages had entered the bacteria
Conclusion: DNA, not protein, is the genetic material.

Reinforcement

1. Harmless R bacteria were transformed into disease-causing S bacteria.
2. phosphorus; phosphorus

Section 8.2

Study Guide

Nucleotide: Refer to Visual Vocab 8.2 for visual answers. Students should label: phosphate group; nitrogen-containing base; and deoxyribose sugar.

1. 4
2. the phosphate group and the deoxyribose sugar; the nitrogen-containing base
3. that it was of uniform width
4. by building models
5. The sugar-phosphate backbone is on the outside. Inside the structure, a base with two rings always pairs with a base with only one ring.
6. A; G

DNA Double Helix: drawing should include sugar-phosphate backbone; nitrogen-containing bases; and hydrogen bonds

7. The sugar-phosphate backbone is like the twisting handrails of the staircase, and the nitrogen-containing bases are like the steps that connect the railings to each other.
8. Because A only pairs with T and C only pairs with G, the amount of A will be equal to the amount of T, and the amount of C will be equal to the amount of G.

Power Notes

Overall shape: double helix

1. deoxyribose sugar
2. phosphate group

Nitrogen-containing bases:
Pyrimidines: thymine, cytosine
Purines: adenine, guanine

Base pairing rules: A pairs with T, C with G

1. H-bonds connect the nitrogen-containing bases in the middle
2. Covalent bonds connect the molecules in the backbone

Chargaff's rules: the amount of A = T and the amount of C = G

Reinforcement

1. A = T and C = G
2. that it was a double helix consisting of two strands an equal width apart
3. the sugar and phosphate molecules; the nitrogen-containing bases

Section 8.3

Study Guide

1. the process by which DNA is copied during the cell cycle
2. nucleus
3. S stage
4. so that every cell will have a complete set of DNA following cell division
5. something that serves as a pattern
6. ATCCATG

7. Proteins help unzip the DNA strand, hold the strands apart, and bond nucleotides together.
8. hydrogen bonds connecting base pairs
9. because each molecule consists of one old strand and one new strand

10. Enzymes unzip the helix.
11. DNA polymerase binds nucleotides together to form new strands that are complementary to the original strands.
12. Two identical DNA molecules result.

13. origins of replication
14. proofreading

15. DNA polymerase is an enzyme that makes DNA by forming bonds between nucleotides. The "-ase" ending signals that it is an enzyme. The first part of the word tells that the enzyme makes DNA by stringing together lots of monomers to form polymers.
16. Replication is the process by which DNA is copied during the cell cycle. Accept any reasonable answer. Students may compare replication to making copies on a copier.

17. Share the best bumper stickers with the class.

Power Notes

General description: replication is the process by which DNA is copied during the cell cycle

1. enzymes unzip the double helix in two directions at the same time
2. nucleotides pair with the exposed bases on the template strands;
3. DNA polymerase bonds the new nucleotides together ;
4. Two molecules of DNA identical to the original molecule result; each molecule contains one original strand and one new strand

1. sugar-phosphate backbone
2. nitrogen-containing bases
3. nitrogen-containing bases
4. newly synthesized strand of DNA

Reinforcement

1. because it makes DNA strands that consist of one original strand of DNA and one new strand of DNA
2. bonds nucleotides together; proofreads

Section 8.4

Study Guide

1. replication (nucleus)
2. transcription (nucleus)
3. translation (cytoplasm)

4. Contains the sugar ribose
5. Has the bases A, C, G, and T
6. Typically single-stranded

7. RNA polymerase

8. A large transcription complex, including RNA polymerase and other proteins, assembles at the start of a gene and begins to unwind the DNA. Using one strand of the DNA as a template, RNA polymerase strings together a complementary strand of RNA. The RNA strand detaches from the DNA as it is transcribed, and the DNA zips back together.

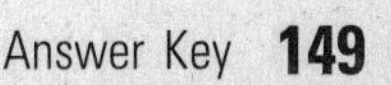

9. **mRNA:** intermediate message that is translated to form a protein; **rRNA:** forms part of ribosomes; **tRNA:** brings amino acids from the cytoplasm to a ribosome to help make the growing protein
10. Both occur within the nucleus of eukaryotic cells, are catalyzed by large enzymes, involve unwinding of the DNA double helix, involve complementary base pairing of the DNA strand, and are highly regulated by the cell.
11. Replication occurs only once during each round of the cell cycle and makes a double-stranded copy of all the DNA in a cell. Transcription occurs repeatedly throughout the cell cycle to make proteins, rRNAs, and tRNAs as needed by a cell. Transcription makes a single-stranded complement of only a particular DNA sequence.
12. mRNA is a form of the DNA message that tells the cell what type of protein to make. rRNA is a key component of ribosomes. tRNA transfers, or carries, amino acids from the cytoplasm to the ribosome.
13. the process of copying a sequence of DNA to produce a complementary strand of RNA

Power Notes

1. DNA
2. transcription
3. RNA
4. translation
5. proteins

DNA: deoxyribose sugar; A, C, T, G; double-stranded
RNA: ribose sugar; A, C, U, G; single-stranded

1. A transcription complex consisting of RNA polymerase and other proteins recognizes the start site of a gene and begins to unwind the DNA
2. RNA polymerase reads one side of the DNA template and strings together a complementary strand of RNA nucleotides
3. The growing RNA strand hangs freely as it is transcribed and detaches completely once the entire gene is transcribed
4. DNA molecule
5. nucleotides
6. newly synthesized RNA strand
7. RNA polymerase

1. messenger RNA (mRNA): intermediate message that is translated to form a protein
2. ribosomal RNA (rRNA): forms part of ribosomes
3. transfer RNA (tRNA): brings amino acids from the cytoplasm to a ribosome to help make the growing protein

Reinforcement

1. that information flows in one direction from DNA to RNA to protein
2. mRNA, rRNA, tRNA; mRNA

Section 8.5

Study Guide

1. the process that converts an mRNA message into a polypeptide, or protein
2. sequences of three nucleotides that code for an amino acid
3. RNA
4. the order in which nucleotides are read; they are read as a series of three, nonoverlapping nucleotides
5. arginine (Arg)
6. stop codon
7. UGG
8. glycine (Gly)
9. Ribosomes, tRNA molecules
10. small
11. large
12. amino acid, anticodon

Cycle Diagram:
A. An exposed codon attracts a complementary tRNA bearing an amino acid.
B. the ribosome forms a peptide bond between the amino acids. It breaks the bond between the first amino acid and tRNA.
C. the ribosome pulls the mRNA strand the length of one codon. The first tRNA exits the ribosome, and another codon is exposed.

13. codons
14. anticodon
15. Stop codons indicate where translation is to stop. (Students may mention that methionine is also a start codon.)

Power Notes

Reading frame: series of three nonoverlapping nucleotides read, in order, by a cell; three different reading frames are possible for each mRNA molecule; codons must be read in the correct reading frame for the correct protein to be made
Start codon: signals the start of translation and the amino acid methionine
Ribosome: the site of protein synthesis; made of rRNA and proteins; catalyzes the formation of peptide bonds between amino acids
Large subunit: binds to tRNA
Small subunit: binds to mRNA
Codon: three-nucleotide sequence that codes for an amino acid
Anticodon: three nucleotides on a tRNA molecule that bind to a complementary mRNA codon
Common language: the genetic code is shared by almost all organisms
Stop codon: three codons that signal the end of a chain of amino acids
Transfer RNA (tRNA): type of RNA that carries amino acids from the cytoplasm to the ribosome; one end has a specific anticodon, the other end attaches to a specific amino acid

1. amino acid
2. peptide bond;
3. large ribosomal subunit;
4. tRNA;
5. codons;
6. small ribosomal subunit;
7. mRNA;
8. anticodon

1. ribosome assembles at the start codon; complementary tRNA molecule pairs with the exposed codon
2. ribosome helps bond the new amino acid to the start codon and breaks the bond between the amino acid and the first tRNA
3. ribosome pulls the mRNA strand the length of one codon; first tRNA returns to the cytoplasm; another codon is exposed for tRNA binding

Reinforcement

1. a sequence of three nucleotides that codes for an amino acid
2. It carries an amino acid from the cytoplasm to the ribosome, where its anticodon pairs with a complementary codon.
3. the ribosome

Section 8.6

Study Guide

1. Regulation allows the cells to better respond to stimuli and to conserve energy and materials.
2. transcription
3. promoter
4. operon, promoter, operator, genes

5. RNA polymerase is blocked by the repressor.
6. The genes are not transcribed.
7. Lactose binds to the repressor protein, and the repressor cannot bind to the operon.
8. RNA polymerase can transcribe the genes.
9. Lactose is broken down.

10. because they express different sets of genes
11. Transcription factors bind to the DNA and help RNA polymerase know where a gene starts.
12. A TATA box is a promoter that is found in almost all eukaryotic cells.
13. a protein that helps control the expression of many other genes and plays an important role in establishing body pattern

Diagram legend: exon; tail; cap; intron

14. An exon is a sequence of nucleotides that is expressed in a protein, whereas an intron is an intervening sequence of nucleotides that will be removed during processing.
15. Answers will vary. Sample answer: A promoter is like a choir director who shows you when to start singing.

Power Notes

Promoter: a DNA segment that allows a gene to be transcribed; helps RNA polymerase find where a gene starts

Operon: a region of DNA that has promoter, an operator, and one or more genes that code for all the proteins needed to do a specific task; typically found in prokaryotes

***lac* operon:** one of the earliest operons discovered; includes three genes involved in the breakdown of the sugar lactose that are all under the control of a single promoter and operator

Without lactose: a repressor protein is bound to the operator and blocks RNA polymerase from transcribing the genes (off)

With lactose: the repressor protein is bound to lactose, which keeps it off the operator, so RNA polymerase transcribes the genes that, in turn, break down lactose (on)

Controlling transcription in eukaryotic cells: transcription is regulated at many points in eukaryotic cells; control of the start of transcription is still an important point of regulation; have unique combinations of regulatory DNA sequences that are recognized by transcription factors; some genes control the expression of other genes and play an important role in development

mRNA processing: occurs after transcription but before mRNA leaves the nucleus. Introns are removed and the exons are spliced together. Introns are intervening sequences of DNA. Exons are sequences of DNA that are expressed in the protein.
A cap is added that helps mRNA bind to a ribosome and prevents the strand from being broken down too quickly.
A tail is added that helps mRNA exit the nucleus.

Reinforcement

1. The lactose binds to the repressor protein, which prevents it from binding to the promoter and blocking the RNA polymerase.
2. promoters, enhancers, and silencers
3. Introns are removed, and a tail and cap are added.

Section 8.7

Study Guide

1. point mutation/substitution; frameshift mutation
2. gene duplication; translocation
3. chromosomal mutation
4. unequal crossing over
5. the attachment of a piece of one chromosome to a nonhomologous chromosome
6. Answers will vary.
7. Answers will vary.
8. noncoding regions
9. premature stop codon
10. no change
11. lack of regulation
12. altered splice site
13. germ cells/gametes
14. no
15. an agent in the environment that can change DNA
16. UV light can cause neighboring thymine nucleotides to break their hydrogen bonds to adenine and bond with each other instead.
17. a change in an organism's DNA
18. a frameshift mutation

Power Notes

Gene mutations: mutations that affect a single gene

Point mutation: one nucleotide is substituted for another; may be fixed by DNA polymerase

Frameshift mutation: involves the insertion or deletion of a nucleotide in the DNA sequence; shifts the entire sequence by one or more nucleotides; throws off the reading frame

Chromosomal mutations: mutations that affect an entire chromosome; affects many genes

Gene duplication: caused by the exchange of unequal segments during crossing over; results in one chromosome having two copies of some genes and the other chromosome having no copies of those genes

Translocation: movement of a piece of one chromosome to a nonhomologous chromosome; are often reciprocal

Potential impact: Chromosomal mutations typically have a large effect on an organism; may result in a disrupted gene or abnormal regulation of genes

Point mutations may result in premature stop codons or amino acids with very different properties from the correct amino acid; may disrupt a splice site; may disrupt a regulatory DNA sequence

Frameshift mutations may result in a completely altered protein or a premature stop codon.

Silent: Some mutations have no apparent effect.

A point mutation may not change the amino acid that is coded for.

Even if a change occurs, the change may be in an intron that is removed and thus has no effect.

A change may not significantly affect the function of a protein if the new amino acid is similar to the correct one or occurs away from the active site or does not influence protein structure.

Mutagens: agents in the environment that can change DNA; some occur naturally (e.g., UV light); some are created by industrial processes

Reinforcement

1. a change in an organism's DNA
2. the reading frame of the codons
3. A point mutation could result in a premature stop codon, or it could change an amino acid that would alter the protein's shape and/or function.

Chapter 8

Data Analysis Practice

1. 3 species with base pairs in the hundreds of millions
2. Students should make a new graph that includes the new data. The new graph should show the number of species with base pairs of 10^5 as 2 and the number of species with base pairs of 10^{10} as 2.

Pre-AP Activity

MODELING DNA STRUCTURE

Pauling-Corey Model: Student diagrams should show a phosphate-phosphate pair at the center (two circles) connecting to a base on either side (two squares), with the bases linking up to the next base in each chain.

Fraser Model: Student diagrams should show a base-base pair (two squares) at the center connected by hydrogen bonds, with phosphates (circles) on the outside, linking up to the next phosphate in each chain.

Watson-Crick Model: This will be similar to the Fraser model, with base pairings of A-T and G-C.

1. The cell is an aqueous environment and it makes sense that the external backbone of the DNA molecule would be made up of hydrophilic components (sugars, phosphates) and the hydrophobic components (bases) would be oriented to the inside, where they would be protected. The cell membrane has a similar orientation, with hydrophilic phosphate heads on the outside and hydrophobic fatty acid chains on the inside.

Pre-AP Activity

INBORN ERRORS OF METABOLISM

1. phenylalanine
2. tyrosine
3. 4-hydroxyphenylpyruvic acid
4. homogentisic acid 1,2-dioxygenase
5. These babies could be fed special diets that contain only enough phenylalanine for them to synthesize proteins, so excess phenylalanine does not accumulate. Students might also suggest that their diets could have a lot of tyrosine.
6. No, tyrosine is broken down in the pathway after the blockage, meaning

it should not accumulate as phenylalanine does. Students might suggest that tyrosine should in fact be part of the diet of children with PKU.

Vocabulary Practice

A. Compound Word Puzzle

1. base pairing rules; Sample answer: A pairs with T, C with G
2. central dogma; Sample answer: DNA to RNA to proteins
3. anticodon; Sample answer: found on a tRNA molecule
4. intron; Sample answer: region of mRNA removed during processing
5. mRNA; Sample answer: a product of transcription
6. mutation; Sample answer: may or may not affect a protein
7. nucleotide; Sample answer: consists of a sugar, a phosphate group, and a nitrogen-containing base
8. exon; Sample answer: spliced together during mRNA processing

B. Find the Odd Word

1. mutagen; Sample answer: Both rRNA and tRNA are types of RNA.
2. replication; Sample answer: mRNA has codons.
3. central dogma; Sample answer: Mutagens may cause mutations.
4. double helix; Sample answer: A frameshift mutation disrupts the reading frame of the codons.
5. bacteriophage; Sample answer: RNA polymerase is one of the major enzymes involved in transcription.

C. Secret Message

1. RNA polymerase
2. frameshift mutation
3. exon
4. ribosomal RNA
5. point mutation
6. mutagen
7. nucleotide
8. translation
9. promoter

D. DNA Adventure!

Across

2. translation
4. nucleotide
5. ribosomal RNA
12. transcription
15. intron
16. double helix
17. base pairing

Down

1. point mutation
3. replication
6. anticodon
7. transfer RNA
8. DNA polymerase
9. central dogma
10. bacteriophage
11. mutation
13. stop codon
14. promoter

Section 9.1

Study Guide

1. artificial nucleotides to sequence genes, copying genes, chemical mutagens, computers, enzymes, bacteria
2. enzymes (from bacteria) that cut DNA at specific nucleotide sequences
3. a restriction site
4. different restriction enzymes have different restriction sites

   Sketch: the blunt end sketch should show a cut straight across a DNA molecule; the sticky end sketch should show a staggered cut that leaves free nucleotides behind. The places at which the DNA is cut should be labeled as the restriction sites.

5. by gel electrophoresis, on the basis of the size of the fragments
6. DNA is loaded into a gel that has a positive electrode at one end and a negative electrode at the other end. The DNA fragments (negatively charged) are pulled through the gel toward the positive electrode. The pores in the gel slow down larger fragments, and smaller fragments will travel a greater distance in a certain length of time.
7. Different sizes of fragments show up as different lines, or bands, on the gel.
8. the lengths of DNA fragments between restriction sites, but nothing about the DNA sequence
9. genetic engineering, studying gene mutations

and diagnosing genetic disorders

10. by cutting the viral DNA

11. DNA is carried by electricity.

Power Notes

Collected from—bacteria
Used for—cutting DNA
Cut DNA at—specific nucleotide sequences (restriction sites)
Can leave—blunt ends (straight cuts) or sticky ends (staggered cuts with free nucleotides)
1. Restriction sites
Gel electrophoresis — separates DNA fragments based on size; smaller fragments travel farther in a certain amount of time than larger fragments
Restriction maps — fragment sizes between restriction sites; do not show anything about genes or DNA sequence

Reinforcement

1. Enzymes from bacteria that cut DNA molecules at specific locations, called restriction sites.

2. It separates DNA fragments based on their sizes; smaller fragments travel toward the positive electrode faster than larger fragments.

3. the lengths of DNA fragments between restriction sites

Section 9.2

Study Guide

1. a technique that makes many copies of a particular segment of DNA

2. without many copies of DNA there is too little to study

3. DNA to be copied, polymerases, nucleotides, primers

4. to start the new strands of DNA

PCR Process: The cycle should include: an increase in temperature and strand separation; temperature decrease and primer binding; temperature increase and polymerases synthesizing the new DNA strands

DNA Changes: The sketch should show 1 to 2 to 4 to 8 to 16 to 32 strands

5. In PCR, polymerase makes more and more copies of DNA as the cycles continue.

6. The primer prepares a DNA strand to be copied.

Power Notes

PCR—technique that quickly copies a desired segment of DNA

1. temperature increased to separate DNA

2. temperature lowered and primers bind to each strand, bracketing the desired segment of DNA

3. temperature increased; polymerases make new strands of DNA

PCR amplifies—every cycle doubles the number of strands of DNA

Reinforcement

1. to rapidly copy a particular region of a DNA molecule

2. a short segment of DNA that acts as the starting point for the copy of DNA

DNA strands separated; primers bind; polymerases copy DNA

Section 9.3

Study Guide

1. representation of parts of a person's DNA that can identify the person at a molecular level

2. different banding patterns on a gel

3. cut DNA with a restriction enzyme and separate the fragments with gel electrophoresis

4. different numbers of repeats in noncoding regions of DNA

5. It shows the sizes, due to the number of repeats, of DNA fragments in specific regions of a genome.

6. In order to identify a particular person with a great degree of certainty there must be a low probability that the DNA fingerprints from two different people randomly match.

7. 1 in 1 million (1/100 x 1/200 x 1/50)

8. the more regions used, the lower the probability that two people would randomly match

9. criminal cases, immigration, species identification, biodiversity studies, tracking genetically modified crops

10. A DNA fingerprint is a distinctive pattern of bands on a gel.

Power Notes

DNA fingerprinting
Based on—noncoding regions of DNA; number of nucleotide repeats in particular parts of the genome; a person's molecular identity; a type of restriction map using gel electrophoresis
Person B—fragments at 2, 3, 4, 5
DNA fingerprints and probability — by investigating several parts of the genome, it is very unlikely that two people would randomly share identical numbers of repeats (multiplying each separate probability to find the total probability of a match)
Uses—criminal cases; immigration; paternity; studying biodiversity; identifying species; tracking GM crops

Reinforcement

1. a type of restriction map that can be used to identify people at the molecular level

2. different numbers of repeats in noncoding regions of the genome

3. to decrease the chance that two DNA fingerprints would randomly match

4. criminal trials, immigration, species identification, biodiversity studies, tracking genetically engineered crops

Section 9.4

Study Guide

1. genetically identical copy of a gene or organism

2. plants, simple animals (regeneration), prokaryotes (binary fission)

3. nuclear transfer; DNA from organism to be cloned is inserted into an unfertilized egg that has had its nucleus removed; egg stimulated and implanted in a female to develop

4. human organ transplants, save endangered species

5. low success rate in cloning mammals, clones imperfect copies, decrease in biodiversity

6. changing an organism's DNA to give the organism new traits

7. DNA that contains genes from more than one organism

8. Plasmids are loops of DNA that replicate separately from bacterial DNA.

Bacteria and Recombinant DNA:
Sketch 1 should show a plasmid and a segment of DNA with the desired gene being cut with a restriction enzyme. Sketch 2 should show the open plasmid and the gene with matching sticky ends. Sketch 3 should show the gene incorporated into the plasmid.

9. an organism that has one or more genes from a different organism inserted into its genome

10. **Bacteria:** *Process*—gene inserted into plasmid, plasmid inserted into bacteria; *Example*—bacteria with human insulin gene
Plants: *Process*—gene inserted into plasmid, plasmid inserted into bacteria, plant infected with bacteria; *Example*—*Bt* (insect-resistant) crops
Animals: *Process*—gene inserted into a fertilized egg, egg implanted in a female; *Example*—oncomouse

11. an organism's DNA is put back together with a new gene from a different organism

12. genes across organisms

Power Notes

Cloning in nature — binary fission, some plants; some simple animals

Mammals— nuclear transfer; low success rate; Dolly the sheep first clone of adult mammal
Potential and controversy — could be used in medical treatments; save endangered species; bring back extinct species; low success rate; decrease biodiversity
Genetic engineering — changing an organism's DNA to give the organism new traits
Recombinant DNA — DNA with genes from more than one organism; genes often inserted into bacterial plasmids
Transgenic bacteria — have plasmid with recombinant DNA; used to make human insulin
Transgenic plants— bacteria with recombinant DNA infect plants; used to make crops resistant to disease, insects, frost
Transgenic animals — gene must be inserted in fertilized egg; used for medical research and to study gene expression
Concerns — long-term effects of GM crops on human health, biodiversity; possible unintended consequences

Reinforcement

1. genetically identical copy of gene or organism
2. used in genetic engineering
3. process of changing an organism's DNA
4. produce an organism with a new trait
5. DNA with genes from more than one organism
6. biotechnology applications
7. loop of DNA separate from bacterial DNA
8. insert new genes into bacteria
9. organism with genes from a different organism
10. GM crops

Section 9.5

Study Guide

1. the study of all of an organism's DNA
2. gene sequencing
3. genomes within and across species
4. find genes related to diseases
5. evolutionary relationships
6. determining the order of DNA nucleotides
7. studies of gene functions, medical research, development and gene expression
8. all DNA from a few people
9. identifying genes, finding gene locations, determining gene functions
10. the use of computer databases to organize and analyze biological data
11. The databases are needed to store and compare the huge amount of information about genomes, as well as provide a way in which to model gene functions and identify genes.
12. small chips that allow the study of many genes and their expression at one time
13. Genes that are being expressed show up as glowing dots on a microarray; the pattern of dots can be compared across different types of cells to compare gene expression.
14. the study and comparison of all proteins in an organism; can include studies of functions and interactions of proteins
15. studies of evolutionary relationships, proteins in human diseases, personalized medical treatments
16. Genomics is related to all of an organism's DNA, proteomics is related to all of an organism's proteins, and bioinformatics is related to biological information.
17. A DNA microarray is a small chip that contains a large number of genes in an organized pattern.

Power Notes

Gene sequencing — determining the sequence of a gene or an entire genome
Genomics — study of entire genomes; can include sequencing of entire genome; compare genomes within and across species to find similarities and differences among different organisms
Human Genome Project — sequenced entire human genome; still working

on identifying all genes, finding their locations, and determining their functions
Bioinformatics — using computer databases to organize and analyze the vast amounts of data that result from studies of genetics (and other biological information)
DNA microarrays — allow scientists to study the expression of many genes at one time; used to compare gene expression in different types of cells
Proteomics — study and comparison of proteins within and across species; used to study evolutionary relationships and human diseases

Reinforcement

1. the study of genomes, including the DNA sequences of the genomes
2. the sequencing of the entire human genome
3. computer databases are needed to organize and analyze the huge amounts of data

Section 9.6

Study Guide

1. to test DNA to determine a person's risk of having or passing on a genetic disorder
2. to look for specific genes or proteins that indicate a particular disorder
3. to replace missing or defective genes to treat a disease
4. inserting the correct gene into the correct cells, regulating gene expression, preventing unwanted interactions with other genes
5. inserting a gene to stimulate a person's immune system to attack cancer cells; inserting "suicide genes" that activate drugs only within cancer cells
6. Genetic screening is the examination of someone's genes.
7. the replacement of a defective or missing gene to treat a disease

Activity: Sample advertisement might include: genetic screening can detect whether a person is at risk for developing or passing on a genetic disorder; it can detect genes related to an increased risk of developing a diseases; it can detect genes that cause genetic disorders; there are tests for only a limited number of illnesses.

Power Notes

Genetic screening — the process of testing DNA to determine a person's risk of having or passing on a genetic disorder; can involve pedigree analysis
Detecting disorders — tests can detect genes that produce disorders such as cystic fibrosis
Detecting disease risk — tests for genes related to an increased risk of cancer, heart disease, etc.
Gene therapy — replacement of defective or missing gene, or adding a new gene, to treat a disease
Methods used
Viruses — genes can be inserted into viruses that are used to infect a person's cells; the desired gene is inserted into the cells by the virus
Immune system — genes inserted to stimulate a person's immune system to recognize and attack cancer cells
Suicide gene — gene inserted into cancer cells that will activate a chemical to kill the cells; normal cells without the gene are not affected
Technical challenges — inserting the gene into the correct cells; controlling gene expression; determining whether the new gene affects the expression of other genes

Reinforcement

1. a process that helps determine whether a person is at risk for developing or passing on a disorder
2. to replace missing or defective genes to prevent or cure illnesses
3. inserting the new gene into the correct cells and then having the gene function properly

Chapter 9

Data Analysis Practice

1. Students should construct a histogram with Cancer Type on the x-axis and Frequency on the y-axis.
2. The frequencies of the different cancers follow the same pattern, but males have a higher incidence for all of the cancers listed.

Pre-AP Activity

DNA FORENSICS: SOLVING A ROYAL MYSTERY

1. 8 is the mother and 3 is the father. If we first assume that 9 is the mother, which would account for marker E in two of the children, there is no single father that could provide markers B and C (for 6). So we know then that 8 must be the mother. Because 8 could only have provided marker C, the father must be the source of both markers B and E in the children. The only father that qualifies is 3.
2. Yes. The mtDNA sequences from the female skeletons (5–9) match that of Prince Philip, while the mtDNA sequence from skeleton 9 does not match (one base is different). The mtDNA sequence from skeleton 3 matches that of James, Duke of Fife, whereas the other male skeleton's mtDNA samples have one or two different bases.
3. Skeletons 5-7, all of them from female children, have DNA fingerprints that are combinations of the DNA of skeleton 3 (adult male) and skeleton 8 (adult female). Mitochondrial DNA of skeletons 5 through 8 showed that all four were related to Tsarina Alexandra's living relative, Prince Philip. Mitochondrial DNA from skeleton 3 matched that of the tsar's brother, Georgij, as well as that of James of Fife.
4. No. We know only that skeleton 9 is not from a Romanov. One could compare mtDNA taken from skeleton 9 with mtDNA sampled from any known relatives of Demidova.

Pre-AP Activity

MEET THE Y CHROMOSOME

1. It has its own repair system that serves as a correct back-up copy in the event that a gene has an error.
2. 1,500 genes on the X. (300 million years x 5 genes lost on the Y chromosome per million years = 1,500.
3. They share many of the same genes.
4. No, because the sex chromosomes had not evolved yet. Sex determination in birds is controlled by a different pattern, not by sex chromosomes.

Vocabulary Practice

A. Stepped-Out Vocabulary

1. identical genetic copy of gene or organism; occurs in nature; used in genetic engineering
2. study of genomes; can include sequencing of all of an organism's DNA; comparisons within and across species
3. the process of testing DNA to determine the risk of having or passing on a genetic disorder; combination of pedigrees and DNA testing; ethical questions about privacy
4. tools that allow for the study of many genes and gene expression; use cDNA; can compare gene expression in different types of tissue
5. study and comparison of proteins; useful in studies of evolution; could help individualize medical treatments

B. Situational Vocabulary

1. b
2. a
3. b
4. b
5. a
6. b
7. a
8. a

C. Analogy Vocabulary Set

1. D5, A4
2. D6, A3
3. D2, A1
4. D1, A6
5. D4, A2
6. D3, A5

D. Vector Vocabulary

1. an enzyme that cuts DNA molecules at specific nucleotide sequences
2. produces fragments of DNA
3. a method that uses electricity to separate a mixture of DNA fragments according to size
4. sorted DNA fragments
5. sorted DNA fragments
6. pattern of bands on a gel that shows the sizes of DNA fragments between restriction sites
7. a type of restriction map that can be used to identify people at the molecular level
8. changing an organism's DNA to give the organism new traits
9. includes several methods and characteristics
10. DNA that contains genes from more than one organism
11. an organism that has one or more genes from a different organism inserted into its genome
12. an organism in which the function of a gene has been disrupted

E. Secret Message

1. primer
2. DNA microarray
3. gene therapy
4. DNA fingerprint
5. clone
6. transgenic

proteomics